| Accident prevention among older people

Accident prevention

among older people

approaches in practice –

a series of case studies in the home environment

Edited by Loraine Ashton

Acknowledgements

All of the information for the case studies has been provided to the HEA through the concerted effort of local practitioners who have directly or indirectly been involved with or responsible for some or all of the local initiatives being reported. They are sincerely thanked for their willingness to provide the information and to share it with others. All of the details were collated in an extremely short time-scale.

The NHSE South Thames is also thanked for funding the HEA to undertake the six month study.

HEA colleagues who have worked on the study and helped with the research and the dissemination of the findings and related practice are also thanked.

ISBN 0 7521 1255 4

© Health Education Authority, 1998

First published 1998
Health Education Authority
Trevelyan House
30 Great Peter Street
London SW1P 2HW

Text composition Ken Brooks
Printed in Great Britain

Contents

Foreword

As we get older, we become more vulnerable to accidents particularly in the home. Accidents are a major cause of death and disabling injury amongst older people. An accident can also rob an older person of their confidence, of their independence and their quality of life. If we can do something to prevent this happening, we would. That is why the Government's public health strategy, *Our Healthier Nation*, includes accident prevention as a target area and asks health professionals, local authority and voluntary sector workers to help Government to reduce the terrible human costs of injury.

As more and more of us reach old age, it becomes increasingly important that we identify how to ensure that our old age is safe and accident-free. This publication shows some of the approaches which can be pursued – some of them traditional, some less conventional – in helping to prevent accidents. Who takes the lead varies: sometimes it is the local authority housing department, sometimes the practice nurse in a GP surgery. What is very clear is the need for collaborative working across the statutory and voluntary sectors, in different settings and involving a variety of professionals. Together we can be effective.

These case studies collected by the Health Education Authority offer helpful pointers for practitioners and policy makers and will be a useful resource for those who have responsibility for developing local strategies in accident prevention. We can learn from each other and share information.

I sincerely hope that all local work will ably contribute to the decrease in accidents among older people and meet the proposed health target. I look forward to hearing of successful and effective practice across sectors.

Tessa Jowell
Minister for Public Health

Introduction

Promoting health and safety in later life

In July 1992, the government published a White Paper *The Health of the Nation*. It set out a strategy for health and established Accidents as one of the five key areas, with a national target to reduce accidents by 33 per cent in the death rate of people aged 65 and over between 1990 and 2005. To date there has been little reduction. The current government's February 1998 Green Paper *Our Healthier Nation* proposes that by the year 2010, accidents (defined as one which involves a hospital visit or a consultation with a family doctor) overall should be reduced by at least a fifth.

It can be argued that promoting the health and safety of older people has not received as much attention as deserved by public health professionals. Nationally accident prevention measures for older people have not been a major issue or well profiled. Whilst localities may have developed an accident strategy or a health-related policy for older people, these have not always matured into an effective implementation stage. Frequently where there have been local interventions they have tended to be undertaken on a piece-meal approach with different agencies pursuing their own initiatives. It is not unusual to discover that there is ignorance of other local interventions and strategies because of the lack of local co-ordination or lack of collaboration. This means there is less impact and effectiveness.

Accidents can be prevented – until recently the overall issue of health, safety and well being of older people has been a neglected area with few health promotion and research initiatives having been undertaken. Whilst it is noted that most people at the age of 65 years are fit and healthy, accidents occur more frequently among older people and form a significant cause of death, disability and contribute to their ill health. Falls actually represent the most common and serious type of home accident in the over 65s age group and can have serious consequences.

Accidents among older people can impact on personal living arrangements, affecting not just the individual but also touching others, be it members of the family or friends who frequently have to take on a caring role once an older person has had an accident. An accident can change the life of an older person significantly leading to the loss of independence and confidence. All of this can further affect an individual's emotional and physical well-being and contribute to low self-esteem. In addition there are usually other direct costs such as providing social care, domiciliary help or residential care.

The size of the problem

Although life expectancy is increasing it does not necessarily mean that extra years gained are being accompanied by healthy, safe and quality lifestyles; a feature of ageing is that there is great variability from one person to another. In particular, the greatest growth in the older population will be among those of 85 years or more; it is predicted that in England this is projected to rise by about 140 per cent over the next 50 years (Joseph Rowntree Foundation, 1996: p. 13).

The prevalence of accidental death among older people is highest for those aged 75 years and over (Office for National Statistics, 1997b). Over 85 per cent of all fatal falls in the home in England and Wales are among people aged over 65 years (Lilley *et al.*, 1995). People of 80 years and over are five times more likely to die as a result of an accident than people aged 65–74 years (*The facts about accidents*, RoSPA, 1993).

Injuries from accidents are responsible for a significant proportion of NHS expenditure: each year in England 300,000 older people present to their local accident and emergency (A&E) departments following an accident. Older people are an important group on which to focus accident prevention advice because 59 per cent of their accidents occur in the home, usually as the result of a fall. Accidents are experienced more frequently as individuals age and are higher among older women for whom safety in the home is particularly important as they do have more mobility problems than men.

The majority of older people live in their own home but injury rates are disproportionate for those in residential care. Frail individuals have a fall rate three times that of more agile older people with falls prevalence and frequency tending to be much higher in the residential and nursing home sector because there is greater frailty of the residents.

The Home Accident Surveillance System (HASS) collects annual data from a rolling stock of hospitals and has indicated that falls account for the largest group of accidents among both age groups and represented 53 per cent of causes of injuries among older people aged 65-74 years, rising to 72 per cent among people over 75 years of age. The number of people 75 years and over whose death has been attributed to a fall is listed as 80 per cent (Department of Trade and Industry, 1997).

Accident data through literature research provide a source of information. However, it is difficult to make comparisons as research is not always defined in the same way and usually there are variables in defining 'older people'. There is no standardised way of defining different accident types. The vast majority of accidental injuries that are reported to GPs or treated at home are excluded from published accidents data. A significant proportion of falls among older people is thought to be under-reported and there is a paucity of local data.

Hip fractures are the commonest major sequelae to falls and over the last twenty years, the incidence has doubled, being twice as common in women as in men and the figures are likely to continue to increase. Hip fractures cost the UK health services an estimated £160 million each year (data quoted by Askham, 1990). There is increasing evidence that calcium supplementation in the diet is protective against hip fracture but evidence relating to oestrogen and hormone therapy and its effectiveness in preventing hip fractures is unproven.

Falls are also associated with multiple risk factors including age-related declines, acute and chronic disease, medications, environmental hazards and lifestyles and psycho-social factors account for an estimated one-third to a half of falls among older people living in the community. As risks are caused by a combination of factors, some interventions may have no effect if the underlying cause is not addressed, for example a medical condition. Older people are heavy users of medication – one-third of the prescriptions in the NHS are estimated to be for them and particular categories such as anti-depressants and hypnotics have been found to be associated with increased risks of falling. Environmental hazards include poor housing, especially related to heating systems with the types and quality of housing inhabited usually being older properties. With many older people being on restricted income it often means that they cannot afford to modify or improve their environment.

In identifying both risks and hazards it can help to determine the most appropriate individual older persons to target. The HEA's qualitative research (Healy and Yarrow, 1998) identifies that the separate elements of risk and hazard are not clearly understood and are confused. Risk evaluation is about determining the importance of a hazard, while a risk is a statistical prediction. The British Medical Association in 1987 defined a hazard as 'a set of circumstances which may cause harmful consequences and the likelihood of its doing so is the risk associated with it'.

Accident prevention research and evaluation

Significant research has been undertaken to investigate the extent and cause of falls among older people with associations being made with lack of mobility, decreased muscle tone and strength, as well as the links between social and psychological problems (Askham *et al.*, 1990). The HEA funded the Effective Health Care review on 'Preventing Falls and Subsequent Injury in Older People' undertaken by the NHS Centre for Reviews and Dissemination, University of York (published April 1996). It specifically covered accidental falls, evaluation of health promotion interventions to prevent falls and reduce injury. The review raised many methodological issues over the evaluation methods as well as the diverse range of combinations covered in studies besides identifying that most research had been carried out outside the UK. It drew a number of conclusions, identifying that the greatest concentration of preventive effort should be on injury, disability and deaths resulting from falls. It suggested that the greatest gain is likely to be from prevention programmes aimed at older people who have one or more risk factors. Utilising the annual screening of older people can provide a good opportunity to target people at particular risk and also to enable the collection of standardised data.

The evaluation of community-based injury and prevention activities has identified some areas as being problematic because:

- there is a lack of data and data collection systems
- little credible evaluation is available due to time and cost
- there is a lack of skills, for example researchers lack fieldwork experience and field workers lack research knowledge
- it is difficult to isolate the effects of particular intervention programmes in a community approach
- there are often many links in the chain and tracking the effects of any single activity can be complex (Benson, 1995).
- the majority of research has focused on individual factors rather than social and material ones with no evaluations of home hazard reduction as the only intervention
- most exercise programmes claiming to be effective for fall prevention have not been systematically evaluated.

Local strategic frameworks – working in alliances

It is imperative that work on accident strategies takes account of the growing numbers of older and frailer people as well as their carers. Quality of life and health outcomes can be improved by better co-ordination of services and recognising that there is the need to directly collaborate with older people themselves if accidents are to be prevented. Older people need to be well informed and be enabled to make the right choices so that they can remain in control of their own lives. Finding ways to directly involve older people in designing, planning and implementation of preventive approaches is very important.

Until relatively recently services in health care and local authorities have tended to be fragmented and it is well documented that there can be difficulties in working across multi-disciplinary and multi-agency boundaries. In developing a strategic framework for local accident prevention activities, it is important to acknowledge the need to promote local alliance working methods. Ideally accident prevention initiatives with and for older people call for arrangements for local working to address joint planning and commissioning structures to best plan for their delivery. Examining existing community care strategies is one way to assess and consider how prevention measures can be introduced or further developed. Assessment and care management processes can contribute to the strategic and innovative practice.

Ideally, localities should provide a forum for sharing practice and raising awareness of initiatives both for the client group and professionals. An older people's forum could help to elicit ideas and help formulate policy and plan services relevant to them. Local Agenda 21 action plans, for example, can allow for older people and/or carers to meet and share knowledge, concerns, thoughts, views and ideas on how to prevent accidents. Members of primary health care teams (PHCTs) have opportunities to meet the target audience and can support, inform and advise older people on how to prevent accidents.

The prevention of accidents and injuries is a complex issue and cannot be the sole responsibility of any one organisation. Both inter-disciplinary and inter-agency working is essential but there needs to be a greater co-ordination of effort to maximise resources and harness energies in order to achieve the best appropriate practice. In order for older people to maximise their independence and safety, a range of support mechanisms and interventions is required including health promotion. This can be enhanced by working through local alliances and identifying and developing appropriate resources and training. The main goal for older people's safety is to reduce incidence of injuries and accidents amongst the over 65s. Those in the position to influence the safety of older people can use the new opportunity provided by the government's expressed thinking in its *Our Healthier Nation* proposals.

Networks to stimulate and support change are crucial. It is important that there is a cohesive approach to accident prevention initiatives for this sector of the population. Coming together locally to strategically work out action plans which ideally relate to other initiatives such as *Health for All, Better Government for Older People, Health Action Zones* and *Best Value* will be appropriate. Indeed it is perhaps timely to consider establishing a locality ageing strategy of which accident prevention is one aspect that contributes to an overall comprehensive strategy in the community.

Checklist for developing or expanding a local accident strategy

As many organisations can be involved in preventing accidents among older people, all need to work in a co-ordinated way to complement each other's role and work as well as to maximise the benefit resulting from working in an alliance. A programme of work based on a sound strategy is required.

An accident strategy should demonstrate its relationship to other local strategies such as an ageing strategy that can be an umbrella strategy for specific issues such as accidents, physical activity and nutrition. The umbrella strategy also needs to take account of the growing numbers of older and frail people in the next two decades. Professional groups, local statutory and voluntary agencies and the private sector should identify their own contributions and specialisms that can support the aims and objectives of the overall and specific accident strategy for older people in their locality.

Having a strategy will better enable the mobilisation of resources. It can also influence how work with organisations can operate and it therefore should be prepared by those whose work brings them into contact with older people as well as older people themselves. Whilst no one strategy will be identical to another the following suggested list should be considered for inclusion and act as a guide to local planners:

- a statement of the rationale of the strategy
- a summary of any national strategy, recommendations, research, indicators or relevant guidelines
- a description of specific and measurable aims and objectives
- a summary of particular benefits for older people in the locality using any available evidence and information from local research/practice

- a statement of principles to involve and work with older people in the planning, implementation and evaluation which should be an underpinning factor of the strategy
- an implementation and monitoring plan including an indication of the timescale of when and how the strategy should be reviewed
- an indication as to how the strategy relates to other national or local areas of work, for example Local Agenda 21, *Better Government for Older People* and how it will support a local ageing strategy
- an indication of its relationship to other local strategies such as nutrition, physical activity, alcohol, the environment
- a list of all the partners involved with the strategy.

An effectively implemented strategy can lead to:

- a greater awareness, cohesion and continuity of work across sectors and organisations
- clearer priorities and targets to which all organisations can work
- fewer gaps in the provision of activities and services
- a systematic review of progress through evaluation of how resources and activities are effectively used.

Recognising that accident prevention is a complex matter, it is important to ensure that during the planning, evaluation and implementation of a strategy mechanisms are devised to involve older people. Empowering older people by developing models of involvement and participation at a variety of levels is key to all prevention initiatives.

Background to undertaking the study

The Health Education Authority (HEA) responded to the National Health Service Executive (NHSE) South Thames proposal to undertake a study which was originally tasked to consider accident prevention work in the primary health care setting. At the suggestion of the HEA the study was extended to identify through a 'mapping' exercise, initiatives being pursued or planned in local authority social services, housing, and environmental health as well as health promotion departments.

The objectives of the national study were to:

- identify and record who has or was planning to undertake accident prevention activities and practice for older people
- identify priorities (if any) of accident prevention work
- identify barriers to the development of prevention initiatives
- identify examples of small manageable work that could be further developed/evaluated.

There were five distinct components to the study comprising:

- a national 'mapping' of activity
- a qualitative research exploring barriers to accident prevention and the training development needs of personnel
- identifying practice and selecting models to become a national network of demonstration sites (case studies)
- disseminating findings and learning through regional workshops
- producing a directory of current practice.

The main method the HEA adopted to collect information was through a postal survey that was designed and piloted before dissemination. To backup the details collected from the survey, the HEA commissioned some qualitative work and the research findings are separately published (Healy and Yarrow, 1998).

Information sharing, need and provision

The fourth stage of the study was the organisation of a series of workshops for multi-professional representatives. These provided the initial mechanism for dissemination of the findings of the national 'mapping' exercise and the qualitative research. Additionally they provided an excellent opportunity to consult with professionals on their own need as well as discussing responses to the government's Green Paper regarding accidents and older people. Also at these workshops some of the identified local practice was introduced to the participants.

The qualitative research findings were confirmed by the feedback from the workshop participants. It mainly covered the need for:

- sharing details on practice both nationally and locally
- national co-ordination and dissemination of practice, research and relevant information
- reliable and standardised statistics, both nationally and, more importantly, for *readily accessible local data*
- information and guidance on how to involve older people in prevention activities
- guidance and training on how to evaluate local programmes of work with older people
- multi-agency training on other pertinent issues
- identifying a local 'lead' organisation to ensure that work was co-ordinated across sectors
- accident prevention work to be undertaken to suit the needs of local agendas
- a national public awareness and educational campaign on accident prevention and safety for older people.

The main barriers to developing interventions for older people have been highlighted primarily as being the lack of resources. Also there is the lack of experience of working with older people and feedback suggested that this was because there was more emphasis put on young people than interventions targeting older people. Professionals also stressed accident prevention cannot be pursued by just one profession or in isolation from other initiatives, as has been indicated through the case studies reported in this publication.

Outcomes of the study

All of the objectives for the six-month study were met and a comprehensive report with recommendations was provided to the funders.

The research and initial practice has been widely disseminated and further work has been commissioned by the Department of Health to build upon the findings of the study.

Accident prevention projects – identified practice

In undertaking the exploratory study, the Health Education Authority (HEA) has identified case studies reflecting a broad spectrum of approaches to accident/injury prevention. The case studies show how, across the country, some localities have several projects being undertaken, indicating the need to address accident prevention interventions with different approaches and with different agencies taking the lead role. The case studies have their own characteristics albeit some with complementary approaches. Often the local players are sub-working groups of larger multi-agency alliance/professional groups as depicted in the Bristol/Avon area for example.

Purpose of the case studies

The main purpose in identifying practice is to provide a closer insight as to how initiatives operate and to share with other practitioners and policy makers details on how local projects have been:

- pursued
- managed and supported
- financed
- evaluated.

The information contained in the case studies includes details on training, alliances, developed resources, research and evaluation and funding support. Each highlights key information to demonstrate the variety of approaches and different alliances that have evolved. They depict the need to address accident prevention work for older people on a very broad perspective. At first glance readers will not necessarily always associate the work with accident prevention as frequently the initiatives do not directly pursue accidents as the key issue.

Building into existing projects, for example, the EPICS scheme in Buckinghamshire addresses the safe and efficient handling of hospital discharge programmes. Encouraging the uptake of physical activity as in Hertfordshire, Herefordshire and Darlington where wardens and others are used to deliver safe exercises to increase mobility of older people and to help prevent accidents are examples of good practice.

Empowering older people themselves to take on roles as in Wiltshire is a good example. The more familiar intervention of a home safety check scheme that can be adopted and incorporated as part of the primary health-care 75+ check scheme is another example of the different initiatives that localities are pursuing. How Health for All (HFA) groups can usefully undertake training work with professionals and older people is illustrated through the Healthy Islington case study. A nurse, as indicated in the Middlesborough case study, is specially employed to deal with older people in general practice as part of a strategy to prevent accidents and good healthy living among older people, with another primary care setting in Cirencester using volunteers to help with the screening process.

The case studies are located in different settings such as GP practices, health centres and community venues. The projects are managed and often financed through different mechanisms such as Health for All (HFA) programmes, part of a health or local authority physical activity project or a commissioned piece of research.

Some of the identified locations have been pursuing their work for some years and quite often with limited resources. Others are relatively new but have seen research and evaluation as key to their initiative.

Criteria for selection

Selection for case study locations were originally set on the following criteria:

- at least one case study in each NHSE region
- cross-section of inner city, urban and rural locations
- existence of monitoring and/or evaluation systems
- partnerships between primary care practices and other agencies
- older people being involved in the planning and implementation of an accident prevention strategy
- a holistic approach to interventions
- targeting older people who are socially or materially disadvantaged.

In the main it was possible to meet the criteria, although the Trent Region did not appear to have any project up and running in spite of reports of accident strategies for older people being in existence. Involving older people from the beginning of the planning process has not always been the case in some of the studies. Disappointingly, the 'mapping' stage of the study did not reveal projects that specifically target ethnic minority groups except for the one reported from Islington.

The sites that have been selected from across England based on the criteria do represent different approaches, different settings and agencies working to enhance accident prevention with older people. They are all at different stages but all have a multi-agency working approach which is crucial for accident prevention work. The selection of case studies reflects this.

In reporting these case studies it is acknowledged that there may be existing and similar style projects around the country. Those selected by the HEA to become a network of demonstration case studies were initially identified through early responses to the postal questionnaire disseminated in November 1997. This was the first phase of the exploratory study that started to 'map' activities across the primary care and statutory sectors.

A national directory and a database of accident prevention initiatives

The HEA intends to further expand knowledge and sharing of information in a number of ways regarding older people's health. Besides the publication reporting the qualitative research aspect of the study as well as this publication reporting on local programmes of work, a national database and a directory are being developed.

Through the information collected in the first stage of the study, it has been possible to computerise the details. The database records, for example, information on who and where there is an accident strategy or other related strategies for older people; where there are hospital discharge schemes; who undertakes the 75+ health checks and details of local projects.

A national directory of projects is being developed and will be regularly updated. It will record other practices and named contacts not included in this publication. The directory will have details recorded from GP practices, health promotion units, local authority environmental health, housing and social services departments in England. All information will be reported on the NHSE regional basis to include local authorities that fall into the regions.

By building upon the case studies depicted in this publication, the HEA is seeking to facilitate the sharing of information both through the in-depth case studies and the directory. The aim is to accelerate the exchange of knowledge and learning to help further encourage the development of accident prevention initiatives for and with older people. Continually learning about outcomes and plans for future work is important.

> Loraine Ashton
> Programme Manager – Older People

References

Askham, J., Glucksman, E., Owens, P. *et al.* (1990) *A review of research on falls among elderly people*. Age Concern Institute of Gerontology; Consumer Safety Unit, Department for Enterprise: London.

Benson, A. (1995) The evaluation of community-based injury prevention activity: the UK perspective. *Injury Prevention* **1**: 116–18.

Healy, J. and Yarrow, S. (1998) *Safe at home?* Health Education Authority: London.

Joseph Rowntree Foundation (1996) *Meeting the costs of continuing care.* p. 13.

Lilley, J.M. *et al.* (1995) Accidents involving older people: a review of the literature, *Age and ageing* **24**: 346.

Office for National Statistics (1997b) *Mortality statistics, Review of the Registrar General on deaths by cause, sex and age in England and Wales, 1995.* Stationery Office: London.

Royal Society for the Prevention of Accidents (1993) *The facts about accidents.*

The case studies

Northern and Yorkshire

Accident prevention alliances in County Durham

Category: Strategic Policy from which specific service development and provisions have been initiated.

Start date: 1992
Completion date: Ongoing

Executive summary

The work described is an evolutionary process to developing a strategic policy approach based on an agreed framework, from which specific services and provisions have been initiated. This programme of alliance working indicates the need to establish a strategic framework that is a shared approach to accidental injury which ensures that the different statutory and non-statutory agencies work together within existing policy structures. Principles for joint working, mechanisms for collaboration in place with clear parameters for target groups and types of intervention have been determined. Levels of accidental injury form part of a three-dimensional framework which allows all agencies to identify their current accidental injury activity in a meaningful way. The formal principles are an attempt to enshrine a specific philosophy to accident prevention and mean that joint working is more than simply an agreement to collaborate on specific interventions.

Background

County Durham is a diverse county with a central populated corridor comprising the urban areas of Darlington, Sedgefield, the City of Durham and Chester-le-Street. To the west of the county, the Durham Dales cover Teesdale, Wear Valley and Derwentside. In this part of the county the population is thinly spread in small towns and villages, many of them post-industrial settlements still surviving following industrial decline starting in the 1920s. To the east is Easington, which borders the North Sea and occupies the hinterland between the major conurbations of Sunderland and Teesside. Peterlee, the main settlement in Easington District, is a new town originating in the post-war new town redevelopment.

Economically, the county has a long tradition of coal and mineral mining, steel production and heavy engineering. In addition, it has always supported both arable and hill farming. In all these areas, the county has suffered greatly from economic decline. There are now no deep shaft mines in operation, which has left East Durham with no large-scale employer.

Steel production, once the mainstay of the Derwentside economy and the sole reason for the existence of Consett, ceased in 1980. The heavy engineering and chemical production plants of Darlington are closed. Outside of the central corridor to the west, the main economic activity is in tourism and farming. Though even here the impact of the Common Agricultural Policy on hill farming has been profound.

Whilst this picture of economic deprivation is similar to any of the former mining areas (as classified by the Office for National Statistics), it would be wrong to see County Durham as being without support. All areas in the county are actively undertaking economic development initiatives and have been successful in securing regeneration funding.

Prioritising accident prevention among older people

Well before the publication of the 'Health of the Nation' health strategy for England the health authorities which were the precursors of the County Durham Health Authority (CDHA) were active in developing, with a range of statutory and non-statutory partners, a joint strategic approach to accident prevention which would allow the development of services. In particular, this strategic work prioritised the prevention of accidental injury in older people over other target groups. The reasons for this are complex, but may be summarised as epidemiological reasons and policy reasons.

The epidemiological priority

The epidemiological reasons are simple. There are 608,000 people who live in County Durham and Darlington. Of these, roughly 95,150 (16 per cent) are older people aged over 65 years and 40,400 (7 per cent) over 75 years. Given the frailty of older people, one of the clear messages from the research base relating to accidental injury in older people is that the consequences of the injury are potentially greater than in other age groups.

For County Durham and Darlington people, this burden of morbidity and mortality amongst older people was formally identified in two need assessments undertaken by the Public Health Department. Two specific exercises were undertaken in the Darlington and Teesdale areas analysing routine sources of data that identified either accidental occurrences or injuries sustained. For both children (under 16 years) and older people (65 years and over) data sets analysed included:

- death registrations and coroner's reports;
- hospital in-patient episodes;
- hospital A&E episodes (including eye clinic data);
- emergency ambulance calls;
- police and highway authority data (based on Stats 19 returns);
- fire brigade data (based on FDR1 returns);
- Health and Safety Executive data.

For children, the data sets also included analysis of the Health Visitor liaison data for the under 5s. Data sets analysed for older people also included:

- mobile warden accident reports;
- sheltered accommodation accident reports;
- a sample of nursing home accident books.

It is not possible to detail the findings from these needs assessments in this case study, but they clearly highlighted the greater burden amongst older people. However tragic the death of a single child, far fewer children die due to accidental injuries than older people. Far more older people are admitted to hospital with fractures, especially fractured neck of femur than for other age groups. The list could continue. Subsequent work capturing other parts of the county – notably in Easington – has not shown there to be any significant differences in the greater burden amongst older people. Nor has it suggested that there is a fundamentally different experience amongst other sub-populations within the county than those identified in the two need assessments.

Drawing from the data sets, a selection of key facts relating to trends was published by the Public Health Department within specific reports entitled: *What's Harming our Children in Darlington and Teesdale?* and *Found on Floor …: A Descriptive Epidemiology of Accidental Injury amongst Older People in Darlington and Teesdale.*

The policy priority

For the CDHA and its precursors, the policy priority to address accidental injury in older people arose within the context of the NHS and Community Care Act (1990). This places an emphasis on the provision of care as close to the person's own home as possible. In addition, the promotion and maintenance of an older person's independence is a basic tenet of community care. If this promotion of independence and care within the home was to be realised, then older people needed to be safe within their own homes. This meant that accident prevention was a key element in community care planning and services.

At the same time, it was clear that accidental injury was also a priority area for action within existing policy for a range of statutory and non-statutory agencies. A clear example is that the issues concerning accident prevention in community care planning and service also effect social service authorities and housing authorities. In addition, a range of statutory duties and responsibilities that have a bearing on accident prevention exist in a large number of agencies and organisations. For example:

- *home safety education* is a statutory responsibility laid on housing authorities (district/ borough or unitary authorities);
- *road safety* is a statutory duty of highways authorities (county or unitary authorities);
- *fire safety* advice is the responsibility of local fire authorities;
- *water safety* is a split responsibility between environmental health authorities, water supply companies and the Environment Agency;
- *workplace safety* is a split responsibility between the employer, the Health and Safety

Executive and the local district/borough or unitary authority.

In fact the confusion over which agency is responsible for what area is great. Agency responsibility for education is often separated from responsibility to enforce regulation; road safety education rests with local county or unitary authorities, whilst enforcement of traffic regulations rests with the police authority.

Strategic framework – a shared approach to accidental injury prevention

In many respects in County Durham and Darlington, the main issue for accidental injury prevention amongst older people was not to create the priority for action. The issue was how to ensure that different statutory and non-statutory agencies could work together effectively within existing policy structures. As a blueprint a single strategic framework was developed in partnership. The framework comprises three main elements:

- a shared approach to accidental injury prevention;
- principles for joint working and
- a mechanism for collaboration.

The framework establishes principles for accidental injury prevention along three main parameters:

- the target groups considered;
- the types of intervention undertaken and
- the levels of injury prevention considered.

The strategic framework formally identified three target groups: children (aged under 17 years); young adults (aged 17 to 24 years) and older people (aged 65 years and over). Whilst the main priority area was identified as older people, it was considered inappropriate to exclude other key target groups. It was also believed that by creating other target groups in the framework it could allow different agencies to see more clearly that what they did, did indeed have a role to play in accidental injury prevention.

The framework adopts the three 'E's of accident prevention intervention:

- *Education* – providing information which tells people about how to avoid accidental injury;
- *Engineering* (or *Environment*) – creating an environment which reduces the chances of an accidental injury or its consequences;
- *Enforcement* ensuring that regulations which reduce risk are enforced.

To this was added a fourth E:
- *Equity* – ensuring that people are not disadvantaged as a consequence of social or economic status.

Finally, the strategic framework identified the three levels of accidental injury prevention at which interventions could occur:

- Primary injury prevention – interventions which aim to stop the accident from occurring;

- Secondary injury prevention – interventions which aim to minimise the immediate consequences of an accidental injury;
- Tertiary injury prevention – interventions which aim to reduce the long-term consequences of accidental injury.

In creating this three-dimensional framework, it allowed all agencies to identify their current accidental injury activity in a meaningful way. For example, it can allow a Durham Ambulance NHS Trust to identify that the provision of front-line paramedic services is a secondary injury prevention, engineering intervention and for CDHA which puts such a requirement into contracts and service level agreements as an enforcement intervention.

Supporting the alliance – principles of joint working

The principles of joint working are clearly laid down in the strategic framework. The most important ones may be summarised for the purposes of this case study as:

- Given the complexity of accidental injury prevention and agency responsibilities, collaboration is essential. It is a necessity, not a nicety.
- Agencies must respect each other's responsibilities and duties. They must support and encourage each other.
- Agencies should do what they are supposed to do first and foremost. In this they can expect to get help, advice and support from collaborating agencies.
- Agencies should collaborate on interventions when it is actually required. There is no point in everyone having to agree to everything before action is taken.
- Agencies need to keep in close contact. Information exchange is essential for effective collaboration and avoidance of duplication.

The formal principles are an attempt to enshrine a specific philosophy around accident prevention. Agencies should be doing what they are supposed to be doing first and collaborating when it makes sense to do so! This forces agencies to consider their own activities first and prioritise resources into these areas – not into collaborating. It also forces other agencies to reflect carefully on whether or not some of their activity is actually appropriate for them to undertake. These principles also mean that joint working is more than simply an agreement to collaborate on specific interventions.

The mechanism for collaboration

The strategic framework clearly identifies membership of an accident prevention alliance as the mechanism for collaboration. To become a member of the alliance, each agency must:

- adopt the strategic framework as a formal policy;
- undertake an internal audit of existing (and potential) accidental injury prevention work within their agency;
- provide a representative for alliance meetings, the representative being a senior officer of the agency;

- provide support, encouragement and advice where appropriate;
- undertake evaluation of activities and interventions;
- share information and data where appropriate.

To facilitate alliance working, the CDHA agreed to provide facilitation by a health promotion specialist with responsibility for accident prevention. To ensure continuity, this was agreed as being part of the standard service specification for health promotion contracts.

Establishing alliances

Establishing accident prevention alliances in County Durham and Darlington has been an evolutionary process. Having a well thought through strategic framework allows initial discussions to take place between agencies. However, to ensure sustainability, the alliances need to develop their own style and approaches to working together (provided that it is in line with the principles for joint working).

Currently there are three alliances covering North Durham, South Durham and Easington. Each was started during 1992/3, though they have differed greatly in the speed of development. Whilst the specifics of developing each alliance have been different, there are a number of commonalities which may be highlighted here.

Recruiting agencies

At the outset recruitment of agencies to become members requires a certain 'critical mass' to allow the alliance to be formed. This was achieved in linking accident prevention to existing joint working arrangements.

In the north of the county, this took the form of working within a local planning team structure which linked accident prevention to health promotion within the community care planning arena. This brought together the (then) North Durham DHA, the local NHS trusts, the social services department, the housing authorities and user/carer representatives. In Darlington and Teesdale, a similar approach soon resulted in an independent alliance for accident prevention being established.

After the critical mass has been achieved, further recruitment comes from either agencies wishing to become associated with success or by individual agency recruitment. In the south of the county, the original Darlington and Teesdale alliance was extended to incorporate Sedgefield and Wear Valley District Councils and became a South Durham alliance. For Easington, recognition that other areas had accident prevention alliances resulted in an approach being made to the Public Health Department to help them establish an alliance.

Finally, recruitment by invitation can be highly effective. However, local experience suggests that it does require the agency being recruited to have an interest in accident prevention which the alliance can help them maintain or improve upon. This approach is very useful when an agency already has a statutory plan or strategy that is of relevance. These usually require a period of external consultation and inter-agency working and are usually looked upon favourably within such plans.

Once recruited, it is vital that the agency does formally adopt an accident prevention policy. Without it, representatives can often find themselves only empowered to attend meetings!

Maintaining agency involvement

The simplest way of achieving this is to ensure that agency representatives are meeting together for good purpose! This means that:

- meetings, which involve all agencies, should be kept to a minimum and be geared towards priority setting and information exchanges rather than intervention/project business. This keeps them informative and useful to all;
- business meetings should be convened between agencies which are collaborating as frequently as necessary – but should always be reported back to all the alliance members;
- representation on alliances has to be flexible. If there are a number of alliances in an area covered by a single agency with only one suitable representative (e.g. the county/district fire prevention officer), then look at ways in which they can become corresponding members of the alliance, or specialist advisors. Don't forget them when they do take up such arms length positions!
- agency progress and representation must be regularly reviewed. Keep the political dimension in mind – agency priorities change over time, agency representatives may need support just to keep their agency on-board;
- an agency is not allowed to be represented by a person who does not have sufficient seniority to undertake the appropriate tasks required of them. Having someone who feels unable to deliver on joint working usually results in that representative focusing on work they can achieve (i.e. not alliance work).

Alliances in action

The three accident prevention alliances in County Durham and Darlington are all – to a greater or lesser degree – effective in developing accident prevention. All have the same core strategic framework and all are facilitated in the same way. At any given time a number of agencies will be active on a range of projects. Given the nature of the alliances it is not actually vital that every agency is involved in every activity; nor is it actually appropriate that they are!

One other point worth noting is that in all that the alliances undertake, the aim is to establish recurrent revenue services. Where this can be achieved by modifying practice within existing budgets, then so much the better. The alliances have agreed that there is little to be gained from simply putting in place a series of time- and resource-limited projects that are unlikely to move into recurrent funding positions. This extends into the field of specific workers relating to accident prevention. There is little point in employing someone to take responsibility for accident prevention. It needs to be part and parcel of an agency's underlying culture – like becoming a 'green' agency or an equal opportunities employer.

As an indication of what is currently under way, the following highlights some of pro-
grammes/initiatives of these alliances.

The North Durham Accident Prevention Alliance

Current membership includes:

- Durham County Council
  - Road Safety and Highways;
  - Social Services;
  - Consumer Protection;
- Durham City Council;
- Derwentside District Council;
- Chester-le-Street District Council;
- North Durham Health Care NHS Trust (Acute and Community);
- County Durham Health Authority;
- Durham Ambulance Service NHS Trust;
- Durham Fire and Rescue Authority;
- Durham Constabulary.

Projects/initiatives targeting accident prevention amongst the older people under way
include:

(i) multi-disciplinary collaboration to introduce effective practice into community healthcare services to prevent falls;

(ii) developing a home repair scheme in Derwentside, linked to home safety checklists for
older people;

(iii) development of a joint NHS/Social Services Department strategy for rehabilitation
services amongst older people (which will include head injury services).

The Easington Accident Prevention Alliance

Current membership includes:

- Durham County Council
  - Road Safety and Highways;
  - Social Services;
  - Consumer Protection;
- Easington District Council;
- East Durham Task Force
- North Tees Hospital NHS Trust (Health Promotion);
- Hartlepool and East Durham NHS Trust (Acute and Community);
- North Durham Health Care NHS Trust (Acute and Community);
- Priority Healthcare Wearside (Community);
- County Durham Health Authority;

- Durham Ambulance Service NHS Trust;
- Durham Fire and Rescue Authority;
- Durham Constabulary.

Projects/initiatives targeting accident prevention amongst the older people under way include:

(i) developing a home repair scheme, linked to home safety checklists for older people;

(ii) redesign of older persons housing to incorporate safety into the basic design of public sector housing (housing association and local authority);

(iii) developing schemes to co-train mobile warden services and community nursing staff in relation to home safety and basic understanding of the health and health care of older people.

The South Durham Accident Prevention Alliance

Current membership includes:

- Darlington Borough Council (Unitary)
  - Road Safety and Highways
  - Social Services
  - Consumer Protection
- Durham County Council
  - Road Safety and Highways
  - Social Services
  - Consumer Protection
- Sedgefield Borough Council
- Teesdale District Council
- Wear Valley District Council
- South Durham Health Care NHS Trust (Acute and Community)
- Priority Healthcare Wearside (Community)
- County Durham Health Authority
- Durham Ambulance Service NHS Trust
- Durham Fire and Rescue Authority
- Durham Constabulary.

Projects/initiatives targeting accident prevention amongst the older people under way include:

(i) a home repair scheme in Sedgefield, linked to home safety checklists for older people undertaken by any alliance professional;

(ii) a discharge management scheme in Darlington which includes home safety checklists and is linked to fast-track repairs/grant support;

(iii) the Get Everyone Moving (GEM) scheme which trains wardens to promote exercise and general fitness in older people.

Main contact

Phil Mackie
Epidemiologist
Directorate of Public Health
County Durham Health Authority
Appleton House
Lanchester Road
Durham
Co. Durham DH7 9QR.

Tel: 0191 333 3307
Fax: 0191 333 3233
e-mail: phil@durphi.demon.co.uk

GEM – Get Everyone Motivated in Darlington

Categories: Education and Training; Service Provision

Start date: April 1997
Completion date: 2-year pilot

Executive summary

Get Everyone Motivated (GEM) is a pilot scheme which aims to provide opportunities for residents and users of the council's sheltered housing schemes and residential homes to take part in physical and leisure activities in order to improve mobility, flexibility and balance and so reduce the incidence of accidents due to falls. The aim is to improve physical, mental and social well-being, improving the quality of life through encouraging the adoption of healthy lifestyles to enable older residents to remain in the community. In developing all of the activities, older people are directly involved in deciding what they want to do.

Background

Darlington Council is part of the South Durham Accident Prevention Alliance which includes the local NHS trusts and the health authority and three adjoining local authorities. An accident strategy is being developed to guide the work of GEM. There are other complementary initiatives to include the Lifestyle Enhancement Activity Programme (LEAP) the council's GP referral scheme which has focused on older people with a dedicated exercise programme. This links into a hospital discharge policy for over-75s and those people who are frail and susceptible when they return home.

Active For Life, a three-year programme, led by the Health Education Authority, was focused on health in older people in 1997/98 and, stimulated by this, a group of senior officers met to discuss how to improve the health of Darlington's older residents and reviewed schemes operating in other parts of the country.

A steering group was formed in April 1997 comprising of the health authority's health promotion unit, housing wardens, supervisors and manager, social services residential homes manager and two tutors/leaders in physical activity from the local leisure centre with the head of environmental and consumer protection leading the group. In discussion an agreed action plan covering a year was drawn up to include:

- recruitment of wardens (through volunteering)
- drawing up a training programme for wardens
- identifying tutors with experience in undertaking exercises suitable for older people and knowing how to modify them appropriately, for example chairobics
- health promotion and organising Look After Yourself courses
- obtaining equipment, for example quoits, bean bags.

It was opportune to recruit wardens into the project as the council was reviewing their role and wished to extend their activities and GEM fitted that requirement. Job descriptions were rewritten to include delivering activities to improve residents' social, physical and mental well-being. The project was launched in September 1997.

Supporting the project

A partnership was formed between the council (environmental health, housing, social services, leisure services, contract services) and South West Durham NHS Trust (health promotion). Reports were submitted to Darlington Borough Council's committees to obtain members' support.

Population

The project reaches approximately 240 residents (6 residential homes with over 40 residents) aged 60 years and over.

Description of work

GEM offers opportunities for residents to participate in various exercise activities – gentle keep fit, stretching, chairobics, exercise to music. In addition there is a variety of leisure activities to include line dancing, walking, yoga, short tennis, badminton, carpet bowls, boules, putting, skittles, table tennis. These are provided in the lounge of the Sheltered Scheme.

Wardens started to tell residents about the project and 'created' anticipation and there were also advanced demands from residents for various activities, in particular line dancing, so activities were devised based on line dancing (without twisting) and notices were used to invite participation.

GEM leaders in organising the activities endeavour to ensure that any of the physical activity schemes are specifically tailored for residents' needs with residents being involved in their choice of activity and its development. The objectives have been to:

- provide a sustainable programme of exercise activity relevant to residents and users together with the specific needs with sheltered housing schemes provided by Darlington Borough Council, housing associations and Age Concern Day Centre;
- train older wardens (volunteers) in the necessary skills to lead, organise and deliver exercise activities;

- monitor and review the success and effectiveness of the scheme through assessment of attendance figures and user surveys;
- gain knowledge of providing such a service and to enable an assessment of 'rolling out' to other locations;
- increase mobility, balance of residents and to reduce incidence of accidents/falls;
- promote physical activity in the inactive.

In the long term it is hoped to contribute to the reduction of CHD and stroke and to contribute to the reduction of fractures associated with osteoporosis as well as raising self-esteem. In the short and medium term it is hoped to contribute to the reduction of hypertension and improve mental well-being by social interaction.

In response to concerns about residents' ability to undertake exercise, an assessment form was drawn up for residents to complete and included an assessment of their own health and ability and medication. These were sent to residents' GPs for comment but GPs did not believe they could 'authorise' exercise so wardens do this themselves. This necessitated additional training being given about older people's health issues.

Insurance is covered by the council's insurers having informed them in advance and gaining approval on the following basis of:

- tutors/leaders must be employees
- must be adequately trained, assessed and monitored
- activity must be in council premises.

Wardens deliver between 1 and 3 sessions per week lasting for about one hour and seeking to provide something for everyone. When the class is finished refreshments are provided thereby adding a social aspect to the activity.

Training

Volunteers, wardens and care assistants from the council's sheltered housing schemes and residential homes attended a series of training and instruction courses from experienced tutors in healthy lifestyle, health promotion and physical activity.

In-house training was developed by health promotion personnel and two LAY tutors based on LAY principles in a 4-day course spread over four weeks. There was specialist input on Health Needs of Older People from the leader of NHS Trust Immediate Response Team amounting to half-days for training on specific health needs of older people.

As part of the support during the training it was planned for wardens to meet regularly (fortnightly) to help put their training into effect, gain confidence and to be assessed by the trainers.

Funding

The partners in supporting the project have contributed officer time and a small amount of money supplemented by a grant of £500 from the Health Education Authority *Active For Life* programme.

The cost of LAY tutors for five full days' training for leaders amounted to 80 hours at £4.80 per hour.

Advice was given to wardens regarding accessing various charities and their funds, for example Age Concern small grants, local Lions Clubs, grants for community activities from the council.

The scheme is provided free of charge to residents initially; however, if a specific activity is requested then a charge may have to be made but it is expected that residents' groups will access various funds to pay for these and provide equipment. A small amount of equipment will be provided free to each leader, for example parachutes, and there will be a central supply which can be obtained on loan such as skittles, putting, boules, table tennis, quoits, balls, bean bags.

Evaluation

To date the following has been evaluated from feedback from leaders/wardens younger than residents.

Residents
- Residents completed questionnaires prior to the scheme and are monitored by the leader as to their improvement.
- Residents were also questioned by tutors.
- There will be a six-month follow-up questionnaire.

Wardens/leaders
- Evaluated by tutors, includes questionnaire and observed teachers producing delivery and actual delivery – feedback during and after activity.

A questionnaire to help with the evaluation has been produced which elicits information in three main sections:
- (i) general information covering levels of fitness, noting any previous slips/trips/falls and any noticed changes of improvement in mobility etc.
- (ii) specific information on leisure-time activities and barriers to taking physical activity etc.
- (iii) details on the views of the activity pursued whilst participating in the GEM project and noting other areas of interest etc.

Outcomes/recommendations

It has been determined since starting GEM that there is a need to:

- develop training materials which takes a long time, and needs to be included at the planning stage
- produce a manual for leaders
- establish a support network to enable leaders to develop and have a refresher training scheme and re-assessment of leaders
- plan for evaluation – be ruthless in demanding evaluation.

The future

This is a pilot scheme and if it is successful it is intended to try and extend it to other council schemes and homes, community centres and other residential homes in Darlington.

The plans are to:

- extend to a further 16 leaders from Darlington Borough Council residential homes in 1998/99
- extend to include training for Age Concern volunteers
- plan for training residents
- expand into housing associations
- expand into private residential homes.

Additionally attempts will be made to try and provide help and information for schemes to be self-sufficient with regard to purchasing equipment as well as seeking long-term funding to secure the training programme.

Contact

Keith Atkinson,
Head of Environmental and Consumer Protection
Darlington Borough Council
11 Houndgate
Darlington DL1 5RF

Tel: 01325 388552
Fax: 01325 388555

Accident prevention in two Middlesborough general practices

Category: Service Provision

Start date: Concept, August 1995 to start of service, November 1995
Completion date: Ongoing

Executive summary

Through pooling resources across practices, a nurse has been employed to carry out the 75+ health checks in patients' homes rather than at the surgery. Previous analysis work carried out in 1994, highlighted the fact that accidents experienced by their older patients were a major issue for the two practices. So screening for accidents in a nurse home visiting service now forms a definite part of the 75+ health check. A full assessment is made with a full back-up support from other primary healthcare team members who also form part of this service.

It is apparent that one of the main reasons for older people refusing help is that they fear having to go into a nursing home, but wish to remain in their own homes and be independent. By arranging for them to have necessary equipment, for example bath seats to help them get in and out of a bath, is so often the simple solution to making them safer in their own homes as well as helping maintain their independence in a safer environment.

There has been an overwhelming response to this new service from patients. Making the nursing service easily accessible both to the patient and the carers has contributed to this success. The GPs are seeing a decreasing workload with this sector and a reduction in calls to patients which in the past have essentially been more of a social matter rather than having to attend for a medical problem.

Background

In 1995, two practices in Middlesborough analysed where they believed their services were deficient and decided upon a new concept to care for older people in their practice. They believed they were unable to offer a full and accurate screening at the surgery and considered that the older patients who did visit the surgery were masking a lot of problems they faced in their home. A nurse who was experienced in working with older people was employed, as this knowledge was considered essential when visiting patients and identifying problems. A personal service was considered fundamental to the success of the scheme, and this has been demonstrated unequivocally.

Description of work

The overall aim is to meet the health and welfare needs of older patients and their carers in the two practices. The specific aims of the project are to:

(i) identify all older patients registered

(ii) assess mobility of older patients with a view to maintaining their independence within the community

(iii) assess medication and ensure patients' understanding and the taking of the prescribed dosage

(iv) identify specific needs and provide health promotion advice

(v) liaise with other healthcare professionals in providing the necessary patient care.

The screening service starts by making an appointment stating the time of the visit, which usually lasts for 45 minutes. This amount of time is required to build a professional relationship with the patient regarding general medical information such as details about weight, height etc. and hearing about individual problems. It has been recognised that failure to pursue symptomatology has led to many home accidents.

The work of the nurse entails identifying hazards around the home i.e. rugs, ill-fitting shoes, unsecured flooring, dark passages and stairways etc. all being given a high priority on the visit. Patients are given advice but realistically the nurse is aware that not all patients will act on the information given. The information and advice is reiterated by the occupational health therapist when a further assessment is necessary.

Advice on how to claim for financial benefits is also part of the role of the nurse. Quite often older people are reluctant to do this because of personal pride. If they are successful, then strong advice is given to spend it on home care, to allow for hazardous tasks to be delegated – thereby reducing the risk of accidents occurring in the home. A Care-Link scheme is essential for providing personal safety and security and this is recommended for all older patients and can be funded from any financial benefits awarded.

A local telephone line has been established to provide a message service to patients and carers offering a link between the nurse and the primary healthcare team. To comply with health and safety regulations, a mobile telephone has been purchased to enable the nurse to access emergency services should the need arise.

Support for the project

The project is supported with the help of other healthcare professionals through buying in services from the occupational therapist, community physiotherapy and community chiropody. As necessary, a dentist and optician are also brought into the project when the nurse identifies the need for home visits.

There is a management team comprising the two fund managers, two lead GPs (one from each practice).

Liaison has been developed with the local social workers. The fire brigade is also supportive and will fit smoke alarms free of charge.

Population

People of 75 years and over in the two practices totalled 4500 patients. A target of 700 patients visited per annum was estimated between the two practices – including telephone communication the figure is currently in excess of this number.

Funding

Development monies were provided from the regional health authority within the fundholding budget and has been granted most years since. The approximate cost of providing this service is currently £40,000 a year.

Training

The nurse has attended several seminars dealing with issues directly related to older people including accidents, nutrition and hydration, health promotion, benefit systems, chronic obstructive pulmonary disorder, etc.

Evaluation

Currently the project is going through an audit system.

Outcomes

Following the rapport between the nurse and patient – a high proportion of patients have acted upon the advice and information given on accident prevention. In addition:

- the budget for prescribing drugs has decreased over the last year
- doctors' workload has gone down with regard to visits from and to older patients and
- other surgeries in the area are seeking information on how to set up a similar service through employing a nurse specifically to work with older people.

The future

Moving into the primary care groups, the two practices are committed to the continuing development of the project. At local meetings the GPs from the two practices are demanding that the service is both retained and enhanced.

Contact

Vicky Philpott
Nurse for Older People or
Avril Dodd
Fund Manager
c/o Dr Levie & Partners
2 Park Road North
Middlesborough
Cleveland TS1 3LF

Tel: 01642 217862
Fax: 01642 245748

Causes of falls amongst older women in Leeds

Category: Research and Audit

Start date: January 1996
Completion date: January 1997 but ongoing

Executive summary

Falls among older women in Leeds are higher than the national figures and Joint Finance awarded monies to the Health For All Accident Prevention Working Group (HFA APWG), commissioning a detailed research project to investigate the causes of falls. This was undertaken with older women who had experienced a fall in their own domestic setting resulting in a fractured neck of femur. Semi-structured interviews were undertaken asking about their perceptions of the cause of the fall as well as about events preceding the fall.

Amongst the findings is the suggestion that terminology used by professionals to describe falls may have to change as it is different from that used by older people and is therefore confusing. A report with recommendations has been produced which in particular highlights the importance of all relevant professionals working together towards reducing falls; it also highlights the fact that separate research is needed to identify the causes of the fractured neck of femurs that were being reported from nursing and residential homes and the hospitals.

Background

Nationally, 60 per cent of all accidents and 30 per cent of all accidental deaths amongst people aged 65 and over are as a result of falls (Riley, C. (1994) *Accidental falls survey: people aged 65+*, Wakefield Health). The most severe falls frequently result in a fractured neck of femur which can lead to complications that result in reduced quality of life and sometimes death (Department of Trade and Industry, (1995) *Home Accident Surveillance System*, HMSO). Nationally the rates of fractures to the neck of femur increase from 175 per million for those aged 65–74 to 1200 per million for those aged 85+.

In Leeds there are approximately five times as many admissions to hospital for fractured neck of femur for women compared with men. Rates per 1000 population in Leeds (both male and female 65+) increased from 5.9 in 1991–92 to 6.54 in 1993–94. Although the admissions rates were remaining steady among men, they showed an increase among older women from 7.7 in 1991–92 to 8.69 in 1994–95 (Information Services, Leeds Health Authority, 1996). These rates compare with the national rates of 6.03 per 1000 (for both men and women aged 65+) in 1993–94 and 7.34 for women aged 65+ in 1993–94.

In the light of the increasing rates of falls for women, the HFA Accident Prevention Working Group, a multi-disciplinary forum working to prevent accidents throughout Leeds, prepared a business case and presented it to Joint Finance.

Description of work

The specific aims of the project were to:

(i) investigate the causes of falls suffered by women of 65 years and over in domestic settings, and which had resulted in a fractured neck of femur;

(ii) conduct a minimum of 45 interviews with older women over a period of several months to ascertain views and perceptions of the cause(s) of the fall(s) from the women involved, and to identify what preventive measures might assist them and others at risk of falls in the future;

(iii) produce a project report with recommendations for the agencies involved in the HFA Accident Prevention Group.

In order to identify the research sample, all women who had been admitted to the orthopaedic ward of Leeds General Infirmary having suffered a fractured neck of femur were recorded between April 1996 and November 1996.

Details were taken from them or their carers to establish where they lived (domestic or not) and whether the injury was from a fall. Interviews were chosen as the research tool to obtain detailed information about the falls the women had suffered. The research tool was chosen over a questionnaire for several reasons:

- open questions can easily be used in order to obtain the women's priorities, and a qualitative account of their experience
- exact details can be obtained by prompts
- any reading or language problems faced by women are bypassed
- responses can be clarified thus permitting a full investigation of the women's perception of the cause of the fall
- questions can be re-phrased if there are misunderstandings.

The interviews contained questions covering the following:

- the recent fall – including activity immediately before the fall and the time and place of the fall
- usual level of mobility – including distance and stability
- previous fall history – including the number and effect of previous falls
- preventative advice – including what advice had been received before the fall

- support levels – including whether there was support at home and if so by whom it was provided
- general health and lifestyle – including medications, smoking and alcohol levels
- previous health assessments – including whether an 'over 75s' check had taken place and where it had occurred
- physical activity – including what was undertaken and the perceptions about the links between physical activity and the prevention of falls
- future prevention – including what was believed to help prevent future falls.

Interviews were carried out within a week of admission to the ward. If women/interviewees were no longer on the orthopaedic ward they were followed up to the rehabilitation wards. Consent was gained from each woman and conversations were taped and analysed by the taking of detailed notes. Once common themes were identified, pertinent quotes were extracted and recommendations drawn from the resulting analysis.

Support for the project

The HFA Accident Prevention Working Group membership includes:

HFA co-ordinator, representatives from the community and mental health trust including health promotion services; local authority housing, road safety and environment departments; fire service and the local under-8s service.

The researcher, who worked as a community nurse and had expertise in working on orthopaedic wards, was employed for ten hours per week to carry out the research and write the draft report. The project was managed by a senior health promotion specialist in the Leeds Health Promotion Service. A management team was also appointed comprising members of the HFA Accident Prevention Working Group.

Research population

- 30 women of 65 years of age and older were interviewed
- 5 were aged 65–74
- 12 were aged 75–84
- 13 were aged 85+ (the eldest respondent, aged 99 years, light-heartedly said that the cause of her fall was that she was 'chasing a man').

Note. This was less than the original number specified because there were fewer women who matched the interviewing criteria than was predicted.

Funding

£7500 was awarded through Leeds Health For All by Joint Finance.

Evaluation

An evaluation was carried out on 10 per cent of the women to ensure that they were not adversely affected by the interviewing procedure.

Research outcomes

There were five main findings:

(i) Most women had suffered a fall before and for a large percentage of the women (45 per cent) their first fall had occurred before they were 75 years old; half of those who had fallen before suffered their first fall less than two years before the injurious one which suggests that there is the need to identify older people who have recently started to fall in order to prevent further more serious falls.

(ii) Only half who had experienced a previous fall described it as a 'fall'. Some reported that they had not fallen before '…well not like this, I didn't hurt myself'. Their preferred terms were 'slip' or 'trip'. With these terms being in common use confusion can occur between professionals and patients when discussing falls prevention.

(iii) Nearly all women (97 per cent) were taking at least one type of prescribed drug. The effects of polypharmacy have been well documented.

(iv) Through many of the interviews there was evidence of acceptance of negative stereotypes about ageing, for example, being less active or having restricted mobility.

(v) From the total, 56 (41 per cent) ward admissions for fractured neck of femur during the research period, came from another hospital ward. Forty-three (31 per cent) lived either in a nursing or residential setting. This compared to approximately 9 per cent of the older population who live in residential nursing care (Wright, F. (1994) *Accident Prevention and Risk Taking by Elderly people: The need for advice*, Institute of Gerontology). This was a disproportionate number from these settings and though it is expected that those living in care settings, do become some of the frailest members of this population this is a high percentage.

Overall the most important finding relates to the terminology used by the women to describe falls which has particular relevance for future initiatives. Professionals may need to change their language to ensure that confusion is avoided. This is especially important in giving preventive advice as older people may not see advice on 'preventing falls' as of relevance to them.

Research recommendations

From the interviews the following has been recommended:

• older people need to be encouraged to notice possible dangers in their home which can contribute to their falling;

• those who have problems with walking should be identified and targeted for fall prevention work;

- use of walking aids needs to be investigated;
- targeting advice after a fall aiming to prevent another;
- preventive advice needs to be given to all older people, including those who are presently well;
- those supporting and caring for older people should be targeted for fall prevention work;
- regular reviews of prescribed medicines should be undertaken by primary healthcare teams (PHCTs) and others who come into contact with older people, e.g. hospital staff;
- older people should be provided with details of drugs they are being prescribed in order to reduce the chance of accidental overdose by over-the-counter medicines;
- the over-75 check undertaken by PHCTs should include advice about fall prevention;
- over-75 checks should be performed at home wherever possible;
- to increase awareness of the preventive benefits of exercise;
- to encourage older people who want to, and are able to, to participate in relevant physical activity;
- targeting advice after a fall should be aimed at preventing subsequent falls;
- that research be conducted into the cause of fractured neck of femur and falls in hospital and nursing and residential homes;
- that hospital and nursing and residential homes be targeted to promote fall prevention.

The future

The report has been widely disseminated and the main findings have been incorporated into the accident prevention work of Leeds HFA Accident Prevention Working Group and also into the commissioning cycle of Leeds Health Authority.

Hospital nurses have been asked to examine their own practice in the hope that changes can be made in their working environment to reduce falls among older people.

Contact

Ruth Burton
Senior Health Promotion Specialist
Leeds Health Promotion Service
St Mary's Hospital
Greenhill Road
Leeds LS12 3QE

Tel: 0113 279 0121 ext 4587
Fax: 0113 231 0185
e-mail: 10513.2471@compuserve.com

North West

Developing preventive services for older people in sheltered housing and in the community in Warrington: a multi-agency pilot project

Categories: Research and Audit; Service Provision

Programme of activities:
Commence January 1998
Complete December 1998

Executive summary

The project is addressing the issue of preventive services by drawing together housing, social and health services to provide a wide range of services delivered in a highly convenient and effective way by using existing sheltered housing schemes. At the same time it assesses the opportunities for extending the health promotion scheme to those living in the community.

The project has used as its basis, a literature search and a local audit of preventive resources.

Description of work

The project is exploring the potential of developing the existing role of scheme managers/wardens in liaising on a detailed basis with health and social service professionals to ensure residents of sheltered housing can continue to manage their lives as independently as possible. The work also entails exploring whether those living outside sheltered schemes can receive agreed support via the manager.

At this stage it should be noted that accident prevention is only one aspect of the overall role of the health promotion project worker. As a pilot project the format of the services developed is under continuous review.

Background

The project was developed in response to the Health Select Committee Report into long-term care (Health Select Committee, 1996) which noted that preventive services can play an important role in delaying and reducing the demand for long-term care. Major research by the Nuffield Institute for Health (Wistow and Lewis, 1996) also laid emphasis on the benefits of collaborative approaches to care suggesting that:

- there was need to test out preventive strategies and community development models at local levels
- there was value in developing 'demonstration projects' which would develop and publicise local models of inter-agency co-operation.

The aims of project are to:

- research local and national resources (for example database searches using Cochrane, MED-LINES and SINLA) to identify the provision of preventive services for older people and identify examples of good practice
- draw together Warrington Community Healthcare (NHS) Trust, local authority housing and social services associations, Care and Repair, GPs, community pharmacists and Age Concern into flexible working arrangements that provide a multi-faceted approach to promoting the physical, psychological and social well-being of older people
- develop a programme of preventive activities that reflect the needs identified by the target population of the project
- provide a social opportunity for older people from which mutual support networks may develop
- encourage community volunteers, scheme managers and care assistants to participate in and take ownership of the activities developed
- measure the extent to which preventive services are significant in reducing admission to institutionalised and hospital care
- measure the extent to which such interventions improve the perceived quality of life of the older people participating in the project
- develop training packages that will enable community volunteers, scheme wardens or care assistants to provide support and guidance regarding maintaining health and enable them to sustain elements of the project beyond its completion.

Project base

The project is based within four sheltered housing schemes which are representative of the variety of sheltered housing provision available in Warrington, i.e. local authority, housing associations, New Town Corporation/social services owned.

Three schemes in the project are owned by housing associations and one by the borough council. One scheme fits the description of 'very sheltered'.

The schemes are situated in:

- *Urban:* inner urban wards with significant areas of pre-1919 housing
- *Mixed:* urban wards one remove from inner areas and composed of older housing and inter-war properties.
- *Others:* outer areas which are distinct villages.

The project is founded on multi-agency and multi-professional collaboration.

Agencies involved include:

housing associations; Warrington Community Healthcare (NHS) Trust – business management and health promotion; local authority – housing, environmental health and social services).

Professionals participating in the project include:

health promotion project worker; community pharmacists (4); care and repair officers; chiropodist; orthoptist; crime prevention officer; sheltered housing scheme managers and a GP.

The project was made known initially to all GPs through the local medical committee. There is also ongoing liaison with GP practices in the four areas where the sheltered housing schemes are located. One GP is acting as overall adviser to the project.

Developing the project

To date a health promotion project worker has taken responsibility for developing a programme of health education activities at each venue. Those specifically related to accident prevention have included health talks about osteoporosis and osteomalacea, home safety and safety in the community, preventing falls and getting up from falls, chiropody treatment and foot care and nutritional advice.

Discussions have been supported with a variety of health promotion material and in many instances an opportunity to access specialist care and/or advice. In addition the programme of health promotion activities also includes a simple programme of gentle exercise and relaxation. Therefore other health issues such as cardiac health, sensory loss, stroke, arthritis, aromatherapy and reflexology and some social and educational opportunities will also be incorporated into the programme.

Care and Repair officers have provided expertise on energy conservation, home safety, home security, welfare rights and benefits which they have introduced at group discussions and followed up with individual consultations for those requiring specialist advice. Care and Repair have also undertaken ninety free home safety checks in a sheltered housing scheme and its surrounding catchment area for older owner-occupiers and tenants of rented properties. They have used these checks to research the incidence and cause of falls amongst participants in the scheme, provide targeted advice and anticipatory guidance about home safety and initiate referrals to agencies for home safety equipment.

Four community pharmacists provide expertise at health promotion talks about commonly used medicines, safe use of medicines, and have disseminated information to groups about the NOMAD system of administering medication. Community pharmacists will also make individual appointments with residents throughout the year to provide more specific individual advice, audit the use of medicines by residents and liaise with GPs about individual difficulties experienced by clients relating to use of their medicines.

Following initial approaches several voluntary agencies have agreed to support health promotion activities through group discussions and presentations. In particular:

- Age Concern have provided information about insurance schemes and their newly opened 'help desk'.
- Arthritis Care have provided information about their organisation and Arthritis Self Care initiatives that have been developed locally.
- Stroke Clubs have provided information and support to a sheltered housing scheme wishing to establish their own 'Stroke Club'.
- Warrington and Widnes Blind Society have provided information about local services and support available for the visually impaired.
- Cheshire Deaf Society have acted as a resource for information about services and facilities available for those with hearing loss.

Needs assessment

The health promotion project worker undertook an audit prior to initiating new activities to itemise the existing provision of preventive services within each sheltered housing scheme and its catchment area as well as within the local authority boundary. This audit used the expert knowledge of local practitioners, statutory agencies and data held by Age Concern that is updated on a six-monthly basis.

Needs assessment within the sheltered housing schemes followed detailed discussion with tenants outlining the broad aims of the project. This was undertaken by the project co-ordinator and the health promotion project worker. Following this 125 residents were asked to complete a simple questionnaire as shown.

Regular meetings

	Interested	Not interested
Gentle exercise	☐	☐
Relaxation	☐	☐
Healthy lifestyle	☐	☐
Talks on specific	☐	☐
health conditions, e.g.		
heart disease	☐	☐
arthritis	☐	☐
dental health	☐	☐
foot care	☐	☐
vision problems	☐	☐
hearing problems	☐	☐
diabetes	☐	☐
use of medicines	☐	☐
Fire safety	☐	☐
Personal safety	☐	☐

	Interested	Not interested
First aid	☐	☐
Welfare rights/benefits	☐	☐
Crime prevention	☐	☐
Quizzes	☐	☐
Bingo	☐	☐
Luncheon club	☐	☐
Whist drives	☐	☐

Short courses

	Interested	Not interested
Aromatherapy	☐	☐
Reflexology	☐	☐
Cooking for one	☐	☐
Reminiscing	☐	☐
Dough craft	☐	☐
Flower arranging	☐	☐
New technology, computing	☐	☐
Fashion for the older person	☐	☐
Photography/video skills	☐	☐
Watercolour painting	☐	☐
T'ai chi	☐	☐
History/archaeology	☐	☐

Comments/suggestions

. . . .

Name . . . .

In all eighty-five questionnaires were returned identifying the interests of the residents. A programme of activities has been developed to reflect their needs and interests.

Involvement of users

The views of users were widely sought in the six-week preliminary consultation period of the project. Users' meetings at the individual schemes were a forum for group discussion about the project and following this a structured questionnaire identified the personal preferences of the tenants of the sheltered schemes.

Users of the project are invited to comment regularly on the quality and variety of services offered. The development of health promotion programmes aims to be a dynamic process that responds to the ideas and needs of the group and as such has been developed on a quarterly basis.

Planning, delivery and evaluation of the project

The following agencies form the steering committee and are engaged in the planning of the programme, overseeing its development and involved with the evaluation aspect:

The University of Salford Housing and Urban Studies Unit; Cheshire Social Services; Warrington Community Healthcare (NHS) Trust; Warrington Hospital Trust; Warrington Borough Council (housing and social services); Grosvenor Housing Association; Warrington Housing Association; community pharmacists and general practitioners and Age Concern.

Population/age/gender

The target groups to benefit from developing preventative services at sheltered housing schemes are:

• the residents (approximately 120) of the four sheltered housing schemes which are two housing association schemes, one social services scheme and one local authority scheme
• people (approximately 100) living in other housing association schemes in the immediate area
• other older people who may be known to general practitioners and Care and Repair.

The project aims to provide a diverse range of preventative measures which will be available to all older people irrespective of age or sex. Activities are currently benefiting those over the age of 60.

Funding

The initial idea for the project was discussed with the Housing Corporation (London) who agreed to support it from the Innovation and Good Practice budget. In addition to the Housing Corporation, North Cheshire Health Authority (joint finance), Warrington Community Healthcare (NHS) Trust and Warrington Borough Council (housing and social services) are all contributing towards the cost of the project.

The budget for the project from these sources is approximately £69,000.

Funding supports the activities of:

Project co-ordinator, health promotion project worker, community pharmacists, secretarial support, Care and Repair and the evaluation of the project.

Evaluation

Options will be tested of home support being organised directly by scheme managers. The agencies that provide the sheltered housing sites for the project will share experiences in a full review of the role of the manager, identifying its cost to residents, and to any older people who may have become recipients of services, and examine issues affecting the future accountability of sheltered housing scheme managers.

Evaluation is being undertaken by representatives from Salford University and will include in-depth interviews with:

- the four individual sheltered housing scheme managers
- housing, health and social care professionals involved in the project.

The emphasis will be on ascertaining their views on the problems and benefits with the implementation of the project and identifying best practice for the future co-ordination and management of preventive services.

A Salford University representative has key involvement in project co-ordination including oversight of the project by a steering committee. In addition he plays an important role in developing new areas of work which were not included in the original project brief, for example:

- home safety check pilot scheme
- new services for older people suffering from chronic respiratory disease.

The following timetable has been identified for evaluation purposes:

An interim review of the project will take place by July 1998.

The evaluation process commences in January 1999 through to March 1999.

The formal report and feedback to agencies will be given by May 1999.

Success of the project will be ascertained through ongoing audit of the structures, process-es and outcomes of the strategies used, i.e auditing:

- the results from a home safety check programme completed by Care and Repair in shel-tered housing, flats, owner-occupied, housing association managed and private landlord 'ordinary' housing in the surrounding catchment area. (These checks were completed in March 1998 and a provisional report will be available in late spring 1998). This will include information about the number of home safety initiatives and referrals initiated as a result of checks and the incidence and cause of falls in the home;
- health promotion sessions in terms of attendance and consumer satisfaction;
- the perceived change in health status of participants in the project;
- the range of preventative interventions that result directly from development of new services.

Positive interventions to date have included:

- access to gentle exercise as a consequence of information about the benefit of exercise and classes being provided at a convenient venue
- referral for grab rails, bath mats and home improvements resulting from home safety checks
- early detection and treatment of varicose ulcers as a result of chiropodist's intervention

- early dental treatment as a result of dental health promotion talk
- aromatherapy treatments for arthritic conditions for which no further medical treatment could be offered
- applications for welfare benefits on behalf of older people attending a group following discussions about welfare rights.

Training

The health promotion project worker, Care and Repair officers, and community pharmacists provide information to the widest audience of older people, through group discussion, demonstration and individual advice.

As the project progresses the health promotion project worker will facilitate the training packages to enable community volunteers, scheme managers/wardens and care assistants to sustain a programme of health promotion activity beyond the completion of the project and also focus on obtaining the earliest detection and treatment of disease.

References

Health Select Committee (1996). *Long Term Care.* Third report of the Health Select Committee. HC 59. Session 1995/96. Stationary Office.

Wistow, G. and Lewis, H. (1996) *Preventive Services for Older People – Current Approaches and Future Opportunities.* Leeds: Nuffield Institute for Health.

Main contacts

Mike Coates
Research Fellow
University of Salford
Allerton Building
Frederick Road
Salford M6 6PU

Tel: 0161 295 2183
Fax: 0161 295 2184

Christine Paley
Health Promotion Worker
Health Promotion Unit
Hollins House
Hollins Park
Winwick
Warrington WA2 8RR

Tel: 01925 664043
Fax: 01925 664044

Accident prevention in older age in the West Pennine area

Category: Strategic approach

Start date: January 1996 – ongoing

Executive summary

A three-year strategy for accident prevention commenced development in 1996 incorporating issues raised at a local conference attended by older people, their carers and professionals. Evidence-based research has been referred to during decisions made about the most effective ways of tackling the causes of accidents amongst older people. Older people have been involved right from the start of the development of the strategy.

Whilst improvements in carers' awareness about accidents and procedures in dealing with falls are important at a community level, it is imperative that the key determinants relating to poverty/inequalities in older age are tackled at a strategic level to include housing design, repair services and access to safety equipment. Already there have been some very useful lessons, outcomes and achievements from this multi-agency strategy, including the development of training for carers, improved data collection/sharing, hospital-based initiatives and a community physical activity programme, for example the provision of t'ai chi classes.

Background

In line with the Health of the Nation strategy, accidents in West Pennine (Oldham, Tameside and Glossop) were considered a priority public health/health promotion issue. Prior to 1995, most of the significant accident prevention work had concentrated on child safety, working with parents, carers, schools and children. Although this valuable work is still continuing, many key agencies caring for older people were keen to develop a co-ordinated, long-term plan for the prevention of accidents, particularly falls in older age (over 65 years).

In January 1996, a Reducing Falls in Older Age conference was held, as a result of multi-disciplinary planning. The day involved older people, their carers and professionals to consider the local concerns about falls and to highlight ways of tackling the problems. These responses have formed the basis of a strategy document, along with findings from evidence-based research, which was developed by a key group of agencies (social services, NHS trusts, Age Concern) who expressed an interest in taking forward the findings from the conference.

Description of project

The strategy document runs from September 1996 to 1999 and takes a wide approach to the main causes of falls (from environmental to medical), based in a number of settings (from community to nursing/hospital). The emphasis has been on primary and secondary prevention.

The aim of the strategy is to reduce the incidence and severity of falls amongst people aged 65 and over. The short-term objectives include:

1 Implementing wider use of home assessments to include a review of medication during the 75+ health checks.
2 Implementing locality-based projects to promote benefits of balance training (for example through t'ai chi).
3 Training staff to demonstrate effective fall prevention measures to older clients/patients.
4 Setting up hospital-based initiatives, for example risk management and reviews of medication on discharge from hospital.

The longer-term objectives include:
1 Improving uneven road/pavement surfaces in public/residential areas.
2 Ensuring residential homes are designed appropriately for older people.
3 Adopting approaches to reduce the incidence of osteoporosis.
4 Incorporating community-based accident prevention initiatives into community development approaches in deprived wards throughout West Pennine area.

The strategy outlines a timetabled action plan and has been planned as a staged approach to tackle priorities.

Outcomes

There have been many learning points from pursuing this strategic approach. Involving all the key agencies who work with older people as equal partners, is imperative for implementation of the strategy. Older people themselves have contributed at points in the planning stages and have been involved in shaping some of the projects, but this must be developed further in the West Pennine area. The main achievements and outcomes to date are as follows:

1 Awareness raising/education

• There have been multi-disciplinary training events for carers on prevention of falls and practical skills for reducing the impact of falls. These were set up between December 1996 and February 1997, with more being undertaken from spring 1998.

- Various presentations to key forums, for example medical advisory groups/joint advisory teams.

2 Data collection

- There have been improvements in collection/retrieval systems, for example with the accident and emergency computerised system.
- Community-based data collection, for example the practice nurse 75+ health check.
- Better sharing of sources of data across agencies.

3 Hospital setting

- There have been risk management/assessment initiatives.
- Guidelines for community nursing staff on reducing falls are being produced to be incorporated into the care package for older people.
- Hip protectors are now available for patients, co-ordinated by physiotherapists (Tameside General Hospital).
- Procedures on stroke wards to reduce falls have been adopted (Royal Oldham Hospital).

4 Community exercise

- A pilot project for people 60+ to improve t'ai chi provision in Oldham has been developed.
- There are two exercise prescription schemes throughout West Pennine which offer a range of activities suitable for people aged 60+.

Most of the projects have been monitored/evaluated in order to make recommendations to key agencies about future work.

Funding

There has been no specified funding for developing the strategy although certain initiatives have been supported by West Pennine Health Authority, Oldham NHS Trust and Community and Priority Services NHS Trust (Tameside).

Future plans

The strategy has long-term objectives to tackle the main environmental determinants of accidents in older age. The challenges concerning inequalities/poverty in relation to accidents in older age have rarely been referred to in evidence-based research to date, and will continue to be a priority in the West Pennine area. For instance, targeted planning/design of buildings for older people and services to improve/repair homes.

In the West Pennine area there are community development initiatives in a deprived ward which include community-based accident prevention work. Including accident prevention with older people in these approaches requires further exploration.

Planning has started with a local tenants management organisation to develop the potential for 'tool libraries' to loan safety equipment, for example DIY/gardening equipment, fire-guards, stepladders. This may be one useful way of improving access to safety equipment and reducing the incidence of accidents in the home.

Main contact

Julie Tolhurst
Senior Health Promotion Specialist
West Pennine Health Authority
Westhulme Avenue
Oldham
Lancs OL1 2PL

Tel: 0161 455 5754
Fax: 0161 455 5768

T'ai chi and exercise on prescription project in Oldham

Category: Service provision

Start date: 4 March 1998 (pilot 10 weeks)

Executive summary

In line with locally identified ways of tackling a reduction in falls and evidence-based research, a pilot has been set up to improve the uptake of t'ai chi amongst Oldham residents of 60+. T'ai chi is being offered by Age Concern as an option as part of the Prescription for Exercise Scheme, referred by practice nurses. The uptake is being monitored, as well as participants' self-perceived benefits and the key agencies' opinion of the pilot scheme. It is intended that if the outcomes are positive, there will be evidence to support wider t'ai chi provision throughout West Pennine.

Background

During a Reducing Falls conference held in West Pennine involving older people, their carers and professionals, improving provision and access to exercise programmes were identified as a priority. There are various research documents highlighting the effectiveness of balance training such as t'ai chi, in reducing the incidence of falls in older age (NHS, 1996). As part of a strategic approach for reducing falls in West Pennine, a pilot project was planned.

The mechanism for the pilot was based on an existing mechanism in place to help improve access to exercise options, and it was decided to offer t'ai chi as part of the Prescription for Exercise Scheme for a pilot period. Age Concern in Oldham were already offering t'ai chi on a fortnightly basis, as part of a leisure facility for people over 55. The key agencies, Age Concern, practice nurses and older people attending the existing classes, were involved in planning the project. West Pennine Health Authority agreed to support the running costs for extra classes to be offered by Age Concern throughout the 10-week pilot period.

Description of work

The aim of the pilot project is to improve uptake of t'ai chi amongst people over 60 years old, living in their own homes, sheltered housing or residential care, throughout Oldham.

The objectives are to:

1 Set up a pilot scheme to refer patients from the Prescription for Exercise scheme to Age Concern t'ai chi classes.
2 Monitor the uptake of t'ai chi places referred through the exercise prescription scheme.
3 Assess participants' perceived benefits from attending t'ai chi classes.
4 Examine the effectiveness of the pilot scheme in encouraging the uptake of t'ai chi.
5 Examine possible options for future t'ai chi, based on recommendations following completion of the pilot scheme.
6 Write up the outcomes and process of the project with a view to publishing.

The process adopted is for practice nurses to refer patients over 60 years of age who will benefit from t'ai chi and have expressed an interest in the classes. A checklist with patient details will be sent to the health promotion specialists co-ordinating the project, for evaluation purposes. The patient takes their record card, entitling them to 5 free sessions of t'ai chi, to the Age Concern class. Age Concern registers all participants.

Performance indicators for Objectives 2 and 4 have been developed as follows:

• Monitor the uptake of Age Concern t'ai chi places (objective 2).
Impact indicator – number of people attending the class each week.
Age Concern to record on the register: name, address, referral from GP.
Health promotion officers (HPOs) to collect the attendance list each week.
Process indicator – number of practice nurses referring patients to t'ai chi – number of patients referred to t'ai chi classes.
Information available on the practice nurses checklist to be sent to HPOs.
Outcome indicator – number of patients continuing to attend after the five-week entitlement.
HPOs compile a list of those patients referred to cross-reference with attendance list after the ten-week period.
HPOs continue to visit monthly for three months after the pilot period (review this indicator after pilot period).
• Examine the effectiveness of the pilot scheme in encouraging the uptake of t'ai chi (objective 4).
Impact indicator – key agencies' view of the pilot scheme.
Age Concern and practice nurses: individual questionnaires.
Participants: focus group discussions.
Process indicator – extent to which the materials have informed people about the project.
Include questions about resources in the interviews/discussions.
Outcome indicator – changes in demand for t'ai chi classes.
Number of people continuing to attend Age Concern classes (or other t'ai chi classes) after the ten-week period.
Include questions about short- and long-term changes in the interviews/discussions.
Age Concern identify changes in the demand for 'non-t'ai chi' services!

Evaluation

Evaluating the project after the ten-week period will be through the participants and the professionals involved, who will be interviewed to ascertain their opinion of whether the aim and objectives of the project have been achieved. There will be long-term monitoring to check how many participants continue to attend t'ai chi and other Age Concern services, after the pilot project comes to an end.

Outcomes to date

The pilot project finished on 6 May 1998 and although the evaluation has not been completed there are already many outcome benefits from the planning stages.

- It has enhanced working relationships with the GP practices already involved in the Prescription for Exercise Scheme and in some cases, due to the t'ai chi option, has encouraged those practices not involved, to join the Prescription for Exercise scheme.
- It has provided an additional vehicle to raise the importance of encouraging suitable exercise options for older people, particularly to reduce the risk of falls, as well as the wider health benefits.

The results of the project will provide extra weight for including t'ai chi as an ongoing option within the Prescription for Exercise Scheme, as well as encourage wider provision throughout West Pennine.

References

NHS CRD (1996) Preventing falls and subsequent injury in older people. *Effective Health Care* 2(4): April.

Main contact

Julie Tolhurst
Senior Health Promotion Specialist
West Pennine Health Authority
Westhulme Avenue
Oldham
Lancs, OL1 2PL

Tel: 0161 455 5754
Fax: 0161 455 5768

Identification of falls within patients over 75 years of age in an Oldham practice

Category: Planned approach

Start date: May 1996
Completion date: Ongoing

Background

The initiative developed from an initial programme of annual screening of patients over the age of 75 years which began in the practice in 1995. The comprehensive health checks were offered to all patients of this age within the practice (approximately 340 patients).

It is known that a large number of falls within the older age group go unreported, and therefore it was decided in 1996 to include information regarding falls within the annual screening programme. The purpose of the initiative was to ascertain whether a planned approach to the problems of falls in the primary care setting can reduce the number of falls.

Description of work

In collecting data, the aim was to approach the causes of falls from a medical aspect for patients based both in their own homes and in nursing/residential homes, and to identify the causes related to the programme of over 75-year-old screening. In doing so, it was hoped to reduce reported falls in the older population by constant review of certain factors known to increase the risk of falling.

A practice nurse was trained to administer screening tools that had been proved to be effective in primary care, using a specially designed assessment form for identifying compliance and appraisal of medication; screening for dementia, depression and alcohol frequency; appraisal of locomotor ability; assessment of vision and hearing; and a physical examination including blood pressure check and pathological tests (initially FBC, renal function, and blood sugar).

Funding

There were no specific funds for the development of identifying falls within the age group in the practice, but initially the screening programme that had been begun in 1995 was funded by West Pennine Health Authority for 12 months and later extended permanently. This was to address the problems generated by the 1990 GP contract by developing a planned care approach to the unmet needs of older people, as opposed to a purely reactionary one.

Evaluation

In the first year of data collection for falls, an informal question at annual screening was asked as to whether a fall had been experienced in the previous twelve months. These results showed that of the 340 patients interviewed:

- 17 per cent had experienced a fall but only 4 per cent had reported the falls at the time to the GP.

Within the data collection for 1997 a decision was taken to record the 'causes' for the falls experienced to see if intervention resulted in reduction of repeated falls. The data collected showed:

- 14.7 per cent of patients over 75 years experienced a fall and 3.5 per cent were reported to the GP.

Of the reported falls, 12 per cent of patients sustained fractures.

Of the patients who reported falls at the annual screening it was found that:

- 10 per cent reported a trip or accident;
- 10 per cent had dizziness thought to be due to ischaemic heart disease already identified;
- 8 per cent fell as a result of vision problems;
- 4 per cent had stability problems associated with previous CVAs;
- 14 per cent fell as a result of unstable diabetes; and
- 16 per cent showed signs of anaemia.

Findings/outcomes

These findings resulted in various strategies linked not only to reducing falls but improving the general medical conditions of patients. Some of the findings from this intervention were:

- Medication was reviewed for poor compliance or necessary changes.
- Referrals were made to opticians regarding vision problems resulting in one patient being registered blind.
- Others were identified as needing additional support from local social services. For example, one patient was suspected of being a victim of abuse and as a result of concerns by both the practice and social services, was removed from home for respite care; on returning home a complex package of care was initiated by the local social services to maintain the

independence and safety of the patient from the abuser.

- Some patients were identified as diabetics due to raised blood glucose levels on testing.
- Others showed low haemoglobin levels.

Future plans

It is intended to continue with the work through:

- continuing the annual screening of the over 75-year-old age group within the practice to include identifying falls;
- recording falls on the computer records of patients (the practice is fully computerised) to enable easier identification of the causes of falls;
- auditing findings annually;
- encouraging patients in taking up the community exercise programme including the t'ai chi programme for increasing strength and fitness, thereby lowering the risks of falling.

Main Contact

Elizabeth Hill
Practice Nurse
Block Lane Surgery
Block Lane
Chadderton
Oldham OL9 7SG

Tel: 0161 620 2321
Fax: 0161 628 5604

Reducing falls in Stockport through promoting physical activity: a multi-agency approach

Categories: Strategic; Education and Training and also Service Provision

Start date: February 1998 with ongoing intentions

Executive summary

Planning a seminar (June 1998) to bring together local key agencies in order to develop a co-ordinated approach to the issue of promoting physical activity to reduce falls among older people.

Background

The profile of accident prevention has rapidly grown in the area but it was noted that activities were occurring in isolation from each other. For example community services in the local authority were developing t'ai chi classes; an Exercise on Prescription Scheme existed; an Over-50s Participatory Safety Event held for a fortnight each August also has a 'falls scenario'; the hospital is auditing and addressing falls on the wards etc. The seminar was an idea instigated by the health promotion adviser for accident prevention (employed by the NHS Trust) who chairs both the strategic and operational multi-agency accident prevention groups in the town.

Because of all of the work being undertaken it was decided to focus on one of the causative factors of falls. Promoting physical activity was chosen because of the wide cross-section of agencies it has the potential to involve, plus the fact that it coincides with the national growth in interest in this topic and in proving its effectiveness. The objectives were:

(i) To provide a half-day seminar for Stockport workers to explore the issue

Participants will be given the opportunity to:

- perceive the scope of the problem of falls nationally
- find out about national research on effectiveness of promoting activity to reduce falls
- share pressures that falls cause locally for agencies and departments
- share what existing action local agencies and departments take to promote activity
- review overlaps and gaps in service provision
- view/sample tasters of local initiatives, for example Dance Elders work, t'ai chi

- consider the way forward for better collaboration and good practice to address the issue.

(ii) To ensure the resultant action plan (i.e. the later stage outcome of the seminar) is a model of good practice

This involved:

- consulting with all the relevant agencies to finalise deadlines, responsibilities and ensure commitment before the plan is published;
- ensuring the plans fit well with existing structures and projects, for example Health Action Zones (HAZ) plans, Health Improvement Programme (HIP), Our Healthier Nation targets, Neighbourhood Strategies, Home Safety Strategy, Stockport Health Promise, Poverty Action Plan, Exercise on Prescription Scheme, Healthy Workplace Award Scheme, etc.;
- where appropriate the health promotion adviser for accident prevention providing a research base/consultancy for agencies involved on issues such as evaluation, targeting, effectiveness, joint working issues.

Planning and programme design

In February 1998 an initial meeting was organised for key players by the health promotion advisers. They represented the following disciplines:

consultants in A & E, rehab medicine, elderly, Healthy Hospital Project, social services, Age Concern, primary healthcare, occupation/rehab. therapy, nursing management, leisure services, Dance Elders work.

The aim of the meeting was to:

- present proposals for a half-day seminar to highlight the issue of how falls in older people can partly be prevented by promoting exercise
- gain agreement on whether the proposal was viable and if so set up a small sub-group to implement the proposal
- begin to appreciate the direction that other agencies and departments are currently taking on the issue of tackling falls or promoting exercise to prevent falls in older people.

A discussion paper detailing background facts was presented, covering:

- demography
- falls and health care
- activity and older people
- how the issue fits with Our Healthier Nation and other key proposals/projects.

It was agreed to proceed with the organisation of a seminar and a sub-group of three people planned the content, working to a very short timescale. The programme they designed covered :

- input on falls, the national picture (by health promotion adviser)

- input on research to prove that an activity programme can prevent falls (paid speaker/ researcher)
- exercise taster (t'ai chi instructor)
- 'This is me you're talking about' (by two active older people)
- 'market-place' stalls – a timed carrousel activity (12 staffed information stalls about relevant local projects)
- workshops – to develop ideas for tackling the issue collaboratively plus a networking fact pack, to take away, compiled from pre-seminar questionnaires which were returned by prospective attendees.

Target audience

The seminar planned to target agencies/staff from:

nursing homes; day centres (voluntary and statutory); social services; practice nurses and GPs; NHS trusts; Care Call; Neighbourhood Health Strategy co-ordinators; retirement course organisers; voluntary care schemes; care of elderly staff; residential care homes; Age Concern; physios/occupational therapists; A &E department; local authority community services, leisure, social services, housing and environmental health departments; district nursing teams; occupational health nurses; Signpost for Carers; Ageing Well Project, housing trusts and volunteer workers.

Funding

It was agreed that no charges for the seminar or lunch were to be made and the venue was provided by the health authority.

Applications were made for awards and sponsorship which was sought from drug companies to fund the event.

Evaluation

It was planned to evaluate the event by examining the quality of the action plan written as a result of the seminar workshops.

The subsequent implementation will be an indicator of the success of the event.

An attempt to gauge the success in achieving increased co-operation between agencies and departments was also planned.

Training

Training development is dependent on the outcome of the seminar and may well figure in the future action plan.

Main outcomes/future plans

It is hoped that the outcome will be an increase in the promotion and uptake of physical activity, increased mobility and fewer falls experienced by older people.

Any action plans are likely to be translated into the Stockport Health Promises which will then enter the formal monitoring mechanisms of the Joint Health Planning Team Structures in Stockport.

Main contact

Gill Dickinson,
Stockport Centre for Health Promotion
188 Buxton Road
Stockport SK2 7AE.

Tel: 0161 456 7435
Fax: 0161 419 9499
e-mail: StockportCHP@compuserve.com

District nurse lunchtime safety education sessions in Stockport

Category: Education and Training

Start date: March 1998
Completion date: December 1998

Executive summary

A bi-monthly programme of lunchtime educational sessions for district nursing teams to raise awareness of adult safety issues and encourage better links with other local services. Two outside speakers at each session, giving a 20-minute input each. District nursing sisters to ensure each team/health centre is represented at each of the sessions.

Background

It was a Stockport Health Promise for 1998 to develop guidelines for district nurses, similar to the health visitor guidelines developed several years ago. However, this model did not translate for district nurses, so these educational sessions were planned instead.

Parallel to these sessions, the risk assessment recording on the patient assessment documentation is being updated.

Objectives

To raise awareness of the following issues and include better links into the following services:

- Community fire safety
- Road traffic accident investigation and new road safety developments
- NW Water/United Utilities extra care schemes
- Gas specialist services and carbon monoxide poisoning
- Stay Put Scheme
- Ageing Well
- Pharmacy and falls
- Importance of activity in preventing falls
- Keeping Warm Keep Well campaign

- Community alcohol service
- Greater Manchester Ambulance Inform Scheme

Planning and Programme Design

A small sub-group of two district nursing sisters, a district nurse manager and the health promotion adviser for accident prevention met in June 1997. There were two further meetings at which it was agreed to axe the original guidelines ideas and instead pursue a programme of lunchtime talks.

The health promotion adviser designed the flier which was disseminated at district nurse team briefings to advertise the calendar of talks for the year.

Criteria/protocol/targeting

The talks are targeted at the district nursing team, e.g. bathing attendants, district nurses.

It operates on a drop-in basis. No pre-booking required. But district nurse management expects every health centre/team to send a representative to each session. It will then be the responsibility of that representative to brief colleagues in their team.

Funding

The event has not incurred any costs. The fliers, venue and drinks are provided by the centre for health promotion.

Evaluation

The following is planned:

- numbers attending will be monitored
- each participant will rate the usefulness of each session
- district nursing sisters will collect follow-up feedback about whether the teams have been able to apply.

Outcomes/recommendations/future plans

If successful the programme could be repeated and opened up to other community staff, e.g. mental health, physiotherapy, occupational therapy, podiatry, learning disability.

Main contact

Gill Dickinson
Stockport Centre for Health Promotion
188 Buxton Road
Stockport SK2 7AE

Tel: 0161 456 7435
Fax: 0161 419 9499
e-mail: StockportCHP@compuserve.com

Stockport over-50s event

Category: Education

Start date: Annual August event (piloted in 1997)

Executive summary

This safety project is similar to Crucial Crew/Junior Citizen, but targeted at people over the age of 50. It is headed by the police and co-organised by Stockport Centre for Health Promotion. Two key aims are: to provide real-life scenarios to enable older people to learn through experience the safe responses to everyday dangers, and second to provide ideas for accident prevention.

Background

In terms of crime, the Police Community Affairs Department has seen a rise in the numbers of bogus officials calling on older people. Crime also figures high on the agenda in the local neighbourhood health strategies commissioned by the health authority. Stockport emergency services reinforce the need to educate and assist older people on basic safety issues.

In terms of accidents, the government in its 1992 document *The Health of the Nation* acknowledged accidents as one of the five key health issues all agencies should be tackling. It set a target to reduce deaths from accidents to the over-65s by 33 per cent by the year 2005. Stockport's local health strategy, *The Health Promise*, outlines how this can be achieved. The Centre for Health Promotion has a lead co-ordinating this strategy. Accident prevention is one of the four health targets now being highlighted in *Our Healthier Nation*.

This initiative was modelled on Stockport Crucial Crew, extending the concept to older people and replicating the success of Stockport's Crucial Crew for children, in terms of both its outcome for visitors and agencies involved. It was piloted in 1997, and since the police have now pledged to run it annually it has been translated into the annual Stockport Health Promise programme.

Description of the project

The event is planned for a fortnight and held at the Stockport College of Higher and Further Education. The objectives are that older people are given the opportunity to:
 (i) become more aware of personal safety
 (ii) consider how they could contribute to crime prevention
 (iii) consider what they can do to avoid becoming a victim of crime
 (iv) learn how to react in dangerous situations
 (v) know what to do in an emergency
 (vi) explore what they can do to prevent accidents within the home and the community.

The above have been identified by agencies in Stockport as issues of concern for the older population.

Within the overall theme of safety, there are two main strands – crime and accidents, and for both the focus is prevention.

In terms of crime, the Police Community Affairs Department is seeing a rise in the number of bogus officials. Crime also figures high on the agenda in the local neighbourhood health strategies commissioned by the health authority.

Planning and programme design

The agencies running the scenarios, the college providing the venue and the WRVS who organised volunteers, attended planning meetings for the pilot.

Groups of over-50s are booked in to attend the event for half a day and are split into groups of six. They then visit seven different scenarios staffed by seven different agencies, each with a different safety theme. Each scenario involves as much participation as possible for visitors to enable them to learn as much as possible from experience. Fifteen minutes per scenario is allowed for, with a five-minute changeover, between each scenario.

Activity for visitors attending is summarised in the flow chart on page 58.

Target audience

The event was planned to be available to any Stockport over-50s group. This younger emphasis was chosen to reflect the need for primary prevention, since it is from this age, for example, that the risk of falling increases. Priority is also given to groups from deprived areas. In the pilot work an attempt was made to invite groups from all 16 neighbourhoods in Stockport.

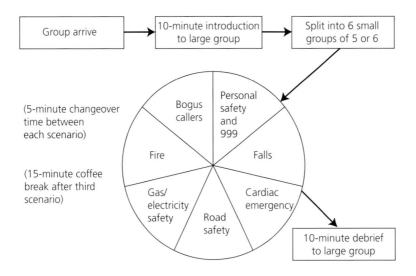

Half-day flow chart

Recruitment

The event is publicised in many different ways:

- agencies who run the scenarios give out flyers to any groups they come into contact with during the year
- local media carry adverts on 'Bill Board', the police page
- local health promotion newsletters advertise it, for example *Stockport Health Focus, Stockport Accident Newssheet*
- direct mailing to over-50s groups

Funding

The direct costs worked out at £1215 for 600 visitors in 1997 (£2.00 per head per visitor). This was only made possible due to the additional sponsorship and support given by agencies and businesses which amounted to £13 875. The venue, refreshments, items for 'goodies' bags and transport were provided in this way.

Evaluation

The event was evaluated on three levels:

1 Content (safety messages)
This was approached in two ways by:

- visitor questionnaire (before and after, multiple-choice style) filled out on the day, twice.
- visitor follow-up evaluation form filled out at home after the event.

2 Process (organisation)
This was investigated in terms of:

- costs
- visitors' perspectives
- agencies' perspectives.

3 Outcome (safety or preventive action taken by visitors)

Visitors who returned their follow-up evaluation form and gave their phone number were contacted again by phone for the purpose of finding out whether they carried out their intentions as stated in their follow-up evaluation form if not, what the barriers were whether any other action had been taken since attending.

A student on placement at Stockport Centre for Health Promotion conducted this third phase of the evaluation as part of her final year degree dissertation.

Full results of the evaluation are available in a report, *Evaluation of the 1997 Stockport Over-50s Safety Event* price £6.00.

Effectiveness

The effectiveness of the pilot which was rigorously evaluated is reflected in the fact that this initiative is now an annual event.

Training

The falls scenario was unique to the other scenarios in that a team of 20 staff (occupational therapists and physiotherapists) were trained to be on the rota working in pairs.

Although a 'briefing' rather than training issue, it was identified from the evaluation that better structuring of the use of volunteers was needed in the form of designated key tasks and written job specifications.

Main outcomes

Key lessons learnt include:

- the high level of action taken by visitors subsequent to attending
- the increase in co-operation and goodwill between agencies involved
- the evident value of building in evaluation right from the beginning.

Future plans

- the event is to continue with slight adjustments, e.g. the last day will be reduced to a half day

- deprived neighbourhoods will be targeted in the future
- care workers will be incorporated differently.

Fuller details are indicated in the report.

Main contact

Gill Dickinson
Stockport Centre for Health Promotion
188 Buxton Road
Stockport SK2 7AE

Tel: 0161 456 7435
Fax: 0161 419 9499
e-mail: Stockport CHP@compuserve.com

Wigan home safety training for home carers: development and delivery of a training package

Category: Education and Training

Start date: May 1995
Completion date: December 1995

Executive summary

The project involved training home carers who work for Wigan MBC Social Services Department in home safety to make them aware of the hazards and related issues that older people face and as home carers how they could assist with solving some of them.

567 home carers were trained out of a potential of 609 (93 per cent) who visit 3500 older people in the borough.

Background

The idea for the initiative was developed during an ad-hoc presentation to older people attending a day centre when it was suggested that it could be beneficial to talk to home carers about home safety. A meeting with the Social Services Department was arranged to discuss the idea and to identify the home safety training needs of carers.

Description of the Project

This training project was planned to utilise the concepts and to base it upon a previously developed, evaluated and successful training package which had been devised for child-minders and play leaders. Its main aims were to:

- raise awareness of issues of safety of older people living in their own homes
- develop home carers' skills in problem-solving techniques on practical issues around safety
- provide practical information on support mechanisms available in the borough to be passed on to older people through the home care network.

Training session – home carers – accident prevention

Time	Teaching method	Resources
$0 - \frac{1}{2}$ hr	Introduction to the course Setting aims and objectives Icebreaker – quiz on home safety	Quiz Teaching pack
$\frac{1}{2} - 1$ hr	Outline of safety issues faced by older people – discussion format	Teaching pack – acetates
$1 - 1\frac{1}{2}$ hrs	Groupwork – real life situations	Group tasks – worksheets
$1\frac{1}{2} - 2\frac{1}{2}$ hrs	Feedback from groups	Discussion
$2\frac{1}{2} - 3$ hrs	Summary Giving out of information packs and details of local contacts.	Information packs and acetates

Note: Break to be included at a suitable time.

Names of partners:

- Wigan Metropolitan Borough Council: Social Services and Environmental Health and Consumer Protection Departments
- Wigan City Challenge
- Wigan Accident Prevention Project

Population

Older people living in their own homes who require additional support from home carers and aimed at both sexes, age usually ranging between 70s and 90s.

Funding

£2 000 was received from Wigan Specialist Health Promotion Services.

The cost of the project mainly involved staff time and also the training resources amounting to an approximate £5 000 for the project.

Also loss of home carers' work time.

Evaluation

The course was evaluated using the following methods:

- questionnaire developed to evaluate the course process

- monitoring of numbers attending the training course
- feedback following a meeting to discuss evaluation of courses with the home care manager
- number of telephone calls received following training on related issues
- general feedback from the courses
- monitoring of long-term related issues.

Outcomes

The initial responses to the course evaluation questionnaire demonstrated that the training had been received positively by the participants. It was also indicated that there was a need to improve group dynamics and participation so the introductory session was amended to include an icebreaker which was devised as a safety quiz.

- Following the courses 21 telephone calls came from homecare staff and their clients relating to the safety issues raised at the courses.
- A follow-up meeting set up with the homecare managers allowed the opportunity to raise many issues that had been brought up during the course and in most instances they were able to be addressed.
- Additionally the health and safety officer for social services produced a homecare booklet that addressed many of the issues raised on the courses together with other health and safety matters.
- An information sheet was developed to provide details of local contacts/health and safety initiatives for older people available in the area.

Other long term related outcomes:

- More recently a Handihelp scheme has been developed by Age Concern which offers practical support to older people as well as home safety checks. This has been supported by Wigan Environmental Health and Consumer Protection Department.
- In 1998 a printed leaflet outlining services available for older people in the borough was produced.
- A similar project with home carers on food safety has been started in 1998. The Chartered Institute of Environmental Health Foundation course is being used and income is being generated so that it can be used to invest in other projects.

It is believed that this project was worthwhile and there were a number of valuable outcomes from the course. One of the valuable aspects of the courses was that the many barriers to accident prevention were identified such as:

- financial issues – either lack of money or lack of willingness to spend money
- reluctance to and/or fear of change
- people not wanting to be disturbed from their daily routine
- reluctance to accept changes in abilities as one ages.

The courses provided the opportunity to discuss possible solutions to these barriers and many other issues.

Difficulties

- It was very time consuming as it required a large amount of organisation.
- Some of the course members had not been briefed about the purpose of the course beforehand and the lesson learnt is that it is important to ensure that participants are made aware in advance of the purpose.

Main contact person

Melanie Durkin/Susan Wilkinson
Wigan Metropolitan Borough Council
Wigan Environmental Health Department
New Town Hall
Library Street
Wigan
WN1 1YN

Tel: 01942 511936
Fax: 01942 511975

West Midlands

Research into the effectiveness of services that aim to reduce falls and fractures amongst older people in Coventry

Category: Research

Start date: 1994
Completion date: January 1996 but ongoing

Executive summary:

A two-year project investigating falls and fall prevention involving home visits to assess falls and also provide prevention information to nearly five hundred older people. It identified that no one thing can cause a fall and often it is a combination of factors which include the environment, vision impairment, amount of medication, physical inactivity, poor nutrition and a history of falls.

The project was evaluated to assess whether the prevention role was useful with the findings suggesting that it was and there is a need and potential to develop an effective programme concerned with falls. Many older people involved in the research indicated that they would welcome and benefit from an annual visit to give advice on falls, benefits and learn of other available services.

Background

Older people now are generally in reasonable health and living independent lives and their expectations of how they will spend their later life are growing. With the introduction of 'Care in the Community' more people are choosing to remain in their homes, when previously they may have been admitted into hospital or into a care home.

An important factor has been the recognition that many aspects of ageing are preventable and reversible although accidents involving older people remain a cause of mortality and morbidity. Although trips and falls among older people are sometimes considered inconsequential, in many cases the causes can be identified and corrected. Of those suffering a hip fracture resulting from a fall, 20 per cent will die within six months and 50 per cent will never regain full mobility. Many falls do not result in serious injury, but being unable to get up does expose the faller to the risk of hypothermia, pressure sores, heightened anxiety and loss of confidence, all of which can lead to further falls.

In Coventry, there are approximately 47,000 people who are aged 65 years or over.

Accidents, in particular falls, are a major problem, and one of the ten health targets for Coventry, set by the Director of Public Health Medicine, focuses on home safety for older people, aiming to reduce the accidental death rate among the over 65s by 20 per cent between 1990 and 2000.

Description of work

The project was designed to identify:

- existing research relating to intervention services that reduce home accidents among older people
- existing services available or provided to older people in Coventry after home accidents
- the sources of cost in relation to home accidents in older people
- possible interventions which could further reduce the number, severity and cost of home accidents among older people
- any changes that may be made to existing services to make them more cost effective in reducing the number of home accidents by using intervention services in ways identified by the research.

A service was organised so that it could be delivered through visiting older people in their homes. A home safety officer (with excellent communication skills and experienced in terms of working in the field of advocating equal opportunities and equity), obtained information about falls and used the opportunity to walk around the home with the person discussing interventions that could minimise the risk of falls. A questionnaire to provide data on various aspects of the lifestyle of older people, their living conditions, numbers of falls was designed. This was completed on the visit. To support the visit, a leaflet which was available in six other languages (Hindi, Gujerati, Bengali, Punjabi, Urdu, Cantonese) on fall prevention was provided. If any concerns became apparent during the visit, these were addressed by making referrals to various professional agencies and voluntary groups.

Contacts were made directly with social services, practice nurses in GP surgeries, and links were made with sheltered housing scheme managers and pensioners' groups. These groups were given short talks on home safety and ways of minimising falls in the home. It was from these sources that most referrals were gained. It was also a useful opportunity to increase awareness of hazards within the home environment to a substantial number of people.

Support for the project

This was supported by a multi-agency accident prevention group with representation from the health authority, the community healthcare trust and the local authority. During the home safety project study, there was liaison with other agencies on a referral basis. They included:

Centre for Integrated Living; Medical Aids (NHD); Age Concern; Coventry and

Warwickshire Community Safety Scheme; Soldiers, Sailors and Airmen's Association; Energy Action Project; community liaison worker (HDU) and the Benefits Agency.

Population

A total of 493 people were visited in their homes, i.e. 1 per cent of the older population living in Coventry, and the following reflects the age, gender and locations reached.

Age range:		Accommodation:	
60–75	118	House	46 %
75–85	226	Flat	43 %
85–89	102	Bungalow	11 %
90–98	49		

Ethnic origin:		Tenure:	
White European	90 %	Owner occupier	218
Irish	4 %	Local authority	223
Indian/Pakistani	4 %	Private landlord	14
Other	2 %	Housing association	27

Seventy per cent interviewed were living alone, 25 per cent with a spouse and 5 per cent with a carer who usually was the son/daughter; 152 were living in the local authority sheltered housing and 41 were with a housing association.

Funding

£35,000 was allocated to the local authority from the Director of Public Health allocated budget for Coventry Health Targets.

Evaluation

Responses indicated that:

- 95 per cent found the visit useful or very useful and 57 per cent had received equipment as a result of the visits.
- over 50 per cent indicated that they had made changes to their home/lifestyle which included moving surplus furniture, taking more care on the stairs using sensible footwear, etc.
- 50 per cent said they had discussed the advice given with friends or relatives.
- 66 per cent had not fallen since the home visit and 15 per cent identified that they had fallen caused by blackout, dizziness, slipped in the bath etc.
- 83 per cent considered they would benefit from similar annual visits.

Outcome findings

There were various findings including:

- 92 per cent of those interviewed had medication prescribed by their doctor with nearly 16 per cent taking five or more different tablets a day. The repeat prescription system seemed to be used regularly without the doctor seeing the patient for several months. In some cases, people had forgotten the reason for the medication.
- Nearly half suffered from arthritis to varying degrees limiting mobility; 73 per cent admitted to having a fall in the past 18 months; 50 per cent used a walking stick and 19 per cent used a walking frame; 47 per cent were housebound.
- 11 per cent interviewed were registered blind and 55 per cent described their eyesight as normal although many needed to wear spectacles.
- Within the home most falls occurred in the living-room, often caused through getting up from a chair quickly and losing balance through sudden movement. Many do not use their bath, preferring to strip wash because they are afraid of falling; 150 people said they tripped or slipped and 273 had received treatment in the A & E department. Note. Professionals may need to change their language in describing falls to ensure that confusion is avoided and especially as older people tend to use the terminology 'slips and trips' rather than 'falls'.
- As a result of the home visits, the officer assessed that the provision of living aids would be beneficial to a further 63 per cent and appropriate referrals were made.

Research recommendations

From the interviews the following was recommended:

1 A falls prevention officer for older people is employed to:

- develop a service of home visits to assess the safety of the home environment and develop a range of interventions such as a safety check, safety modifications and referral to agencies;
- work in partnership with other agencies to develop and make accessible to older people, practical and acceptable advice and information on which to base decisions on safety;
- develop in partnership with other agencies, awareness raising amongst the general public of the avoidable threat posed by accidents in the home.

2 The development of a physical activity programme, including balancing exercises and how to get up after a fall, should be considered. This could be developed in liaison with the falls prevention officer.

Other recommendations:

- 75+ health checks by GPs, picking up health issues that may lead to falls should be reinstated.
- risk assessment relating to falls is included in assessment of service provision in older people's homes, for example domiciliary care.

- many falls occur in the street and uneven paving may contribute to this, therefore this is a matter that should be addressed.
- separate financial resources are provided for living aids.

The future

The report has been disseminated across Coventry. Currently a programme that complements the Coventry Community Plan is being developed. Coventry City Council has also been selected to be a pilot area for the Better Government for Older People initiative, and this research will inform this specific initiative.

Contact

Rachel Flowers
Principal Health Development Officer
Health Development Unit
Housing and Environmental Services Directorate
Broadgate House
Broadgate
Coventry CV1 1NH

Tel: 01203 832586
Fax: 01203 831831

Wham! Bam! – bend and mend: a lifestyles improvement programme for older people in Herefordshire

Category: Education and Training

Start date: September 1997
Completion date: May 1998

Executive summary

This is a lifestyles 'cascade' training scheme which contributes to the Herefordshire Local Agenda 21 Action Plan. It is organised by a multi-agency steering group with the lead taken by the environmental health department for wardens from sheltered accommodation, carers from residential homes and individuals who work with groups of older people. Part of the scheme is to encourage post-retirement people to undertake simple physical activity as a way of promoting health and preventing accidents.

Over an eight one-day-a-week course, participants cover a number of topics to include, safety, first aid, stress control, physical activity, food hygiene, environmental issues and other related health matters.

Background

Local Agenda 21 has often been considered only as an environmental campaign and 'WHAM! What Happens After Me?' is the Herefordshire Action Plan for Local Agenda 21, which is encouraging a sustainable and meaningful way of life. WHAM! BAM has been devised to highlight the social and health aspects of sustainable development with particular emphasis on an often overlooked group of society, the 'third age'.

The idea for the project was as a result of reading about the 'Full of Beans' initiative begun by St Albans District Council (see page 107). A steering group met in September 1997 to discuss the project idea and to decide how to proceed. One option was for the project to be run directly by the officers with a group of older clients; or training could be carried out with appropriate personnel who have contact with older people using a 'cascade' method and run on the lines similar to training 'Look After Yourself' (LAY) trainers. The latter option was decided upon and the aims and the objectives were accordingly developed.

Recruiting the trainees was done through direct contact made with local residential care homes and wardens. An advertisement was also placed in the local press for anyone in contact with older groups of people who was interested in joining the pilot group of trainees. Seventeen trainees attended the first training session.

Support for the project

The steering group of officers from four district councils representing the housing, leisure and environmental health departments, the health authority health promotion unit, the Herefordshire Hospitals NHS Trust dietitian and Leominster Housing Association have contributed to the development of the project.

Description of work

'Bend and Mend' refers to the promotion of physical activity for better health, the prevention of accidents and the improvement of social interaction by the introduction of a wide range of topics. The specific aims of the project are to:

- improve the quality of life for older people;
- train trainers who are carers or have contact with older people to introduce exercise and other 'socialising' activities.

The objectives are to:

- run courses/sessions promoting activities which might improve the quality of life for older people;
- encourage increased physical activity as a way of promoting health and reducing the risk of accidents;
- inform participants of the importance of a balanced diet and the hygienic preparation of food;
- instruct participants in simple first aid and resuscitation techniques;
- illustrate the importance of environmental issues on sustainable development and establish ways of influencing the future;
- promote increased social interaction amongst groups of people.

It is a course spread over eight one mid-week days comprising mixed sessions which in total add up to 37 hours. The trainers are officers from the steering group with expertise in specialist areas. Participants are trained to run courses/sessions on many lifestyle improvement topics whilst developing their own knowledge and skills in many areas.

The course format is:

Day One   Setting the scene, purpose format
           Physical activity – need, motivation and theory
           Physical activity – levels, practice

Day Two   Exercise practice
            Stress control theory and relaxation
            Home safety

Day Three   Exercise practice
            Role of the trainer and adult learning
            Relaxation practice
            Diet – healthy eating

Day Four   Exercise practice
            Food hygiene
            Local Agenda 21
            Relaxation practice

Day Five   Exercise practice
            Resuscitation and simple first aid
            Environmental and social issues

Day Six   Exercise practice
            Looking at health
            Teaching techniques
            Relaxation practice

Day Seven   Exercise practice
            Teaching techniques, contacts, running courses
            Revision
            Relaxation practice

Day Eight   Exercise practice
            Evaluation and course evaluation

The course is run in a community hall at a local authority sheltered accommodation site, with one hour for lunch which is provided. Participants will be evaluated as trainers throughout and be certificated as appropriate. Once the training is completed, participants will be expected to run at least one course for a community group.

Training

The aim of the training course is to establish a network of trainers who can provide WHAM! BAM training to older people throughout Herefordshire. The objectives are:

1 To train carers/people involved with older people to have knowledge, competence and confidence to work with older people to improve the quality of lives.
2 To this end trainers should:

• have an understanding of the importance of physical activity in maintaining health and preventing accidents and be able to demonstrate suitable levels of physical activity for older people

- know the basis of a balanced diet and the hygienic preparation of food
- be able to demonstrate simple first aid and resuscitation techniques
- know the meaning of sustainable development and the links between social, economic, health and environmental issues and their effect on the world and the people in it
- know the risks and hazards which cause accidents in and around the home
- develop skills in communicating and motivating older people to participate in WHAM! BAM.

3 To disseminate further the scope of Local Agenda 21, sustainable development and WHAM! amongst the community.

The trainees are evaluated on their competence throughout the course and in some instances through 'testing' at the end of the course e.g. presentation skills.

The first courses to be run by those who have been trained have not yet been identified.

Course difficulties/outcomes

The project was originally designed for training wardens of sheltered accommodation plus representatives of the community within that site. After much discussion it was decided to restrict the training to wardens only. In practice this did not materialise due to their work-load and time commitments etc. There was limited response and it was then decided to extend the opportunity for training to carers from the local residential care homes as well.

The local authority fitness consultant withdrew from the project at the last minute and a substitute had to be found in a few days.

It had initially been thought that the trainees should have background knowledge of phys-iology etc. and some of the theory behind exercise to give them adequate knowledge for providing physical activity. This aspect proved daunting to many of the trainees and the steering group acknowledges now that Look After Yourself (LAY) training would have been sufficient. If trainees then had groups of clients who wished to develop the physical activity side, Extend trainers could be used.

Two trainees gave up mid-course, leaving fifteen in number which is a good size group with which to work. There was some initial trepidation on behalf of the trainees that they would be expected to become expert trainers with a minimum of training themselves. This fear was overcome as the weeks passed and it was emphasised that encouraging groups of older people to be more physically and socially active need not be so formal as at first thought. Trainees will be expected to be competent and confident to run 'sessions' on the different aspects of the course but not to do anything they are not happy about.

Funding

All participating agencies provide their time at no charge. A grant of £500 from the Hereford and Worcester Rural Development Area Small Projects Fund was awarded for incidentals such as printing and the payment of a fitness consultant, with other funding coming from the district councils and the Herefordshire Health Authority.

The total cost of the course is approximately £1000.

Evaluation

This is the first course and it is being evaluated in order to determine whether it is sufficiently successful to continue. To date the trainees seem to have been motivated and keen but whether this can be passed on to older people in the community has yet to be established. The trainees and the trainers are determined that this scheme will be a success. The new trainers will offer courses to take on board the perceived needs and requirements of their group of older people so that the essence of the programme for them will remain but with appropriate adaptations.

Contact

Bobbie Hadley
Policy Officer
Environmental Health and Trading Standards
The Herefordshire Council
PO Box 233
Hereford HR1 2ZF

Tel: 01432 261838
Fax: 01432 261982

Home safety check schemes in Gloucestershire and Hereford

Category: Service provision

Start date: 1983 and ongoing

Executive summary

Gloucestershire Home Safety Check Scheme was created to address the problem of home accidents and now forms an integral part of the Gloucestershire accident prevention strategy. The scheme helps, in particular, adults over 60 years to identify potential hazards in their homes. It also provides the means to eliminate many of them.

The work is carried out by teams of two fieldworkers making domiciliary visits to clients. In company with the client, the home is toured, checking for faults and hazards. Where hazards have been identified, workers, where possible, make rectifications either at the time or on a return visit.

In one Herefordshire group practice referral for a home safety check is routinely offered as part of the 75+ check. Visits are made only by request and appointment. No canvassing or cold calls are ever carried out. The workers are employees of Severn NHS Trust, not volunteers.

An accident prevention strategy for the county has been developed by the Gloucestershire Accident Action Group (GAAG) to ensure that as far as possible all agencies can work towards commonly agreed targets for preventing accidents.

Background

The risk of accidents is one of the clearest instances of health inequality in society. Poverty, bad housing and a poor environment all make accidents more likely, with accidents causing a higher number of deaths in the over-65s than in any other age group. Besides falls, other important causes of injuries among older people are burns and scalds.

Nationally, falls are a major cause of mortality and morbidity among older people. Accident rates in Gloucestershire are generally higher than national and regional rates and although there is considerable year-on-year variation accident prevention has enjoyed a high priority from the health authority.

National studies regarding falls among older people have demonstrated the higher risk of falls in this age group with 55–65 per cent of accidents being due to this cause. In people aged 65+ years in the community, between one-third and one-half suffer one or more falls in a year (DTI, 1995). This points to the importance of raising awareness of this risk in old people themselves and in the primary healthcare teams and other services.

The combination of frequency of falls with osteoporosis leads to much greater risk of fractures. Older people who have suffered a fall are more likely to have further falls. This gives a clear indication for following up patients seen in accident and emergency departments or discharged from hospital following a fall. It is important to identify and correct modifiable causes of weakness and unsteadiness.

In addition to intrinsic factors the environment also plays a key role. Fitted carpets and securely fastened floor coverings are important, as is good lighting and appropriate hand rails. These are all more likely to be absent if people are living in poverty.

This Home Safety Check Scheme was originally developed in 1983. Funding for practical work to promote health became available under the Manpower Services Commission initiative to return the unemployed to work. The requirement for the work to be practical precluded the usual health education activities.

Although pre-dating the formation of the Accident Action Group, the Gloucestershire Home Safety Check Scheme was created to address the problem of home accidents since, perhaps surprisingly, no agency has a statutory responsibility for home safety.

Population

The target groups are older people defined as retirement age (94,000 in Gloucestershire) and people with disabilities.

Description of the work

The overall aim is to reduce the level of injuries occurring in the home. The main objectives are to:

- reduce the level of environmental hazards in at-risk households
- increase the number of safety devices in use in low-income households
- increase awareness of home safety.

The objectives of the Gloucestershire Home Safety Check Scheme have been incorporated into the overall accident strategy because it was agreed that the activities of the scheme addressed important issues and provided direct action to address inequalities.

The scheme works with teams of two (usually one male and one female) workers making domiciliary visits to clients and, whenever possible in the client's company, touring the home checking for faults and hazards. Where hazards have been identified, the workers will point them out to the householder and, where possible, make rectifications, either at the time or on a return visit. No charge is made for any of the work carried out, nor for small items such as fuses, plugs and flexes. Where a repair is beyond the abilities of the team alternative recommendations are made or actions taken, such as a referral to a 'Care and Repair' or 'Staying Put' organisation.

Visits are made on a request- and appointments-only basis. Referrals are received from a variety of sources, for example wardens of sheltered housing, older people's groups, media articles, health and social services professionals. A recent innovation is to canvass people with a 'lifeline' support.

In many cases a lack of safety equipment is noted, most commonly smoke detectors. The scheme can provide these items at cost price and carry out any necessary fitting free of charge. Smoke detectors are purchased by the hundred direct from Dicon, the manufacturers. The detectors are always fitted on ceilings as this is the most efficient location and normally a 10-year lithium battery is used to avoid the problems associated with changing batteries at high level. Detectors are supplied with the batteries for £7.50. In cases where there is apparent hardship the scheme is usually successful in obtaining charitable funding to provide essential safety equipment. It is considered that priority should be given to those with telephone alarm systems as these are likely to be at higher than average risk.

One GP practice is currently targeting patients over 75 routinely by writing to them to inform them of the Home Safety Check Scheme. The scheme then sends the client a specially prepared leaflet. This system appears successful in targeting the most vulnerable groups. Because the posts are part-time the workers tend to bring a wide range of experience with them, for example an ex-fire officer and two ex-police officers are currently employed.

There are at present four fieldworkers in Gloucestershire engaged in carrying out checks for older people, each working three days a week and carrying out 1200 checks per year. In addition four workers are based in Hereford. Transport used is a combination of leased and trust-owned vehicles.

Training

The training provided takes the form of a general induction plus more specialised training by a range of agencies, including the trust's own works department. Training includes basic electrical, gas and fire safety, as well as information on benefits and the special health problems likely to be encountered by older people.

Although most of the staff employed have no formal electrical qualifications they are deemed to be competent to undertake simple repairs. In addition the scheme now has access to the services of a qualified electrician. When necessary specialist training is given. All the Gloucestershire staff have received training in portable appliance and electric blanket testing.

Much of the training is 'on the job'. As the scheme has a tendency to attract recruits from the public sector it was found that communication skills and an ability to present information on subjects, including accident prevention, were already present. Other training is given to meet the needs of staff when necessary, in particular fieldworkers have attended training sessions given by health visitors. Recently all staff attended a multi-disciplinary age awareness training day.

As the workers are employees it means there is a lower staff turnover and thus lower training costs than is often the case with volunteers.

Needs assessment

No formal needs assessment has been carried out. Consultation with the Department of Trade and Industry over the creation of the scheme indicated the significant types of hazard to be found in homes and enabled a checklist to be prepared. Age Concern were also consulted regarding the acceptability of the proposed scheme to older people.

Partner organisations

The Gloucestershire Accident Action Group as a multi-agency group includes representatives from Gloucestershire Health Authority; Gloucestershire County Council's road safety unit, trading standards and education departments and fire and rescue service; Gloucestershire Constabulary; the local authority environmental health departments; the Health and Safety Executive; Gloucestershire Ambulance Service; Severn and East Gloucestershire NHS Trusts.

The scheme is multi-agency, although within the Severn NHS Trust. It is managed by a committee drawn from these agencies. The group meets every four months and receives a report on activities and performance including checks carried out, rectifications made and equipment supplied. The management committee also provide the forum for planning future developments.

The scheme currently also operates on an agency basis for the health authority in Hereford, the operation of which is monitored by a similar management group. This project, Herefordshire Home Check, will only be funded by the health authority until the end of June 1998 when it is hoped that it will be continued by the new unitary Herefordshire Council.

The main point of contact with the district and borough councils is their housing and environmental health departments, building on links already established by the health promotion department. This process has been helped by the fact that both the manager and assistant manager of the scheme are familiar with local authority grant application systems and are able to present the case for funding in a manner known to be acceptable to the local authorities.

Funding

The scheme is funded by Gloucestershire Health Authority, the County Council (Public Protection) and all six district councils.

Currently this stands at a total of £79,000 per annum.

The health authority funding of £34,000 is regarded as recurring, as is the annual contribution of £12,000 made by Gloucestershire County Council under a service level agreement.

Funding is in the 'base budget' of three district councils – two award an annual discretionary grant and one is presently negotiating a service level agreement.

The balance of the funding is on the basis of one 'share' from each of the district councils and two 'shares' from the county council, although some councils pay less than their share on occasion.

Note. The total includes a contribution of £21,000 from Gloucestershire Health Authority for three staff specialising in child safety. Although these staff work almost exclusively on child safety, their employment does have the advantage of an economy of scale in terms of administrative costs.

Herefordshire Health Authority currently pay £37,000 p.a. for Herefordshire Home Check.

Evaluation

Although there are no published studies showing the direct benefit of the precise type of home safety check scheme that is being operated, other systems of equipment provision have been evaluated. In addition, the type of equipment supplied and fitted has been proved to save lives. By targeting those who have the greatest need, equipment is supplied to those least likely to purchase it themselves. Also the faults found and rectified by the workers are types that have been shown to cause death and injury.

A study carried out in 1989 on past clients of the Gloucestershire scheme between one and two years after they had received a check showed a reduction of 60 per cent in self-reported injury over the past year when compared with a 'control' group of people who had applied for, but not yet received, a check. The survey was conducted by telephone and relied on the client's memory for the injury data and so had methodological limitations; however the results were encouraging.

A literature review by the Nuffield Institute (1996) did establish that home visits to assess and modify environmental risk factors, amongst other things, can be effective in reducing injuries.

An examination of the records of checks revealed almost twice as many hazards in households referred by health professionals than those who self-referred which has lead to an emphasis on increasing the proportion of professionals making use of the scheme. Changes in referral rate and faults found will continue to be monitored. Rectifications made, advice given and consumer satisfaction are continuously monitored.

Future plans

Because of the potential the scheme has to address health inequalities it is planned to continue for as long as funding permits.

There is a demonstrable need to improve the targeting of the home visits and improved co-operation of health and social service professionals is essential to this.

Having a firmer funding base will assist long-term planning, and service level agreements are being sought with those local authorities which have yet to agree them.

It is likely that further evaluations will be carried out in the future in order to satisfy the health service requirement for evidence of effectiveness.

The latest information on the Gloucestershire Home Safety Check Scheme can be found on the website: http.homesafety.co.uk

References

Department of Trade and Industry (1995) *HASS listings for 1993 for males and females aged 50 and above for falls.* Consumer Safety Unit, DTI.

Nuffield Institute for Health (1996) Preventing falls and subsequent injury in older people. *Effective Health Care* NHS Centre of Reviews and Dissemination, University of York 2(4).

Main contact

Philip Bennett
Health Promotion Gloucestershire
Gloucestershire Royal Hospital
Great Western Road
Gloucester GL1 3NN

Tel: 01452 394596
Fax: 01452 395135

Warwickshire falls prevention programme (pilot study)

Categories: Service Provision; Education and Training

Start date: Autumn 1996 (planning)
September 1997 (First pilot)
April 1998 (Second pilot)

Completion date: December 1997 (First pilot)
July 1998 (Second pilot)

Evaluation: Ongoing

Executive summary

This project grew from the desire of the Warwickshire Action on Accidents Alliance – which incorporates many disciplines – to reduce the number of falls and/or the severity of injuries caused by falls among older people. Careful consideration of published research and observation of an established falls clinic in Walsall led the Alliance towards adopting a holistic approach to be based in the community.

The project has pursued a broad approach incorporating exercise, risk assessment, and information and advice about related topics such as diet, medication, footcare and services available. The scheme incorporates a specially designed exercise programme and opportunities to socialise. Consisting of three 'courses' of ten weekly sessions, each 'programme' has been run by nursing staff from a selected GP practice in each of the three locations. Each practice invited twelve to fifteen patients aged 70 or older who were judged to be at risk of falling to participate in the programme.

The essence of the project is that it is community-based, adaptable and non-threatening. Although not a scientific study, there are indications that the programme can and has reduced risk factors for falls. Professionals involved with the project have been convinced of its value, and there are already plans to cascade training in this approach to all involved in the care of older people. Several new initiatives have been prompted, including a pilot project in nursing homes.

It took several months and many meetings to agree a protocol for the programme. This detailed preparation has been vital for the success of the project and to assure continuing commitment and support.

Background

In Warwickshire half of admissions for falls during the year 1996/97 were for fractured femur and over 400 fractured femur cases were treated during a year. With an average stay in hospital of 21 days, the costs of treatment are high. The hotel costs for these patients are more than £2 million, so the full cost to the health authority of treatment and rehabilitation is considerable. It has been estimated (from national data) that 20 per cent of fractured femur patients die within a year of their accident, and a further 20 per cent lose their independence as a result. Many more suffer restricted mobility. Clearly the consequences of a fall resulting in a fractured femur are usually much more serious and costly than just the initial treatment for the injury.

Fear of falling (or of falling again) can often affect an older person's enjoyment of life, by making the person less confident about going out or carrying on with their previous activities. Unfortunately, it is observed that almost all of those who suffer a serious fall will fall again within the year. The *Health Survey for England 1996* estimated that for every 100 men aged 75 or over there would be 8 major falls and 51 minor falls during the year. Equivalent figures for women aged 75 and over were 15 major falls and 44 minor falls. (These numbers may not represent the actual number of people affected, as some may have more than one fall during the year.) These figures illustrate the huge potential for fall injuries; and for the *prevention* of some of these incidents, or at least a reduction in the severity of injuries if a fall occurs.

The Action on Accidents group were eager to target this source of injury in older people. Research into identifying risk factors for falls and effective prevention is extensive and has been reviewed as an *Effective Health Care Bulletin* in April 1996. Some of the most frequently cited potential risk factors were:

- Nutritional status: Vitamin D and calcium deficiency.
- Environmental   (Thought to account for between a third and a half of falls in
  hazards: the community.) Loose carpets, baths without grab-handles,
                           poor lighting, unsafe stairways, ill-fitting shoes, etc.
- Medication: Certain drugs, especially antidepressants and hypnotics, are associated with increased risk of falling. Interaction of drugs can also increase risk.
- Lack of exercise: Weak muscles, poor balance and gait. Also accelerated bone loss.
- Ageing changes and   Deterioration of vision, cognitive impairment, etc.
  medical condition:

There is limited evidence for any single intervention, but:

1   Balancing, low impact aerobic, or muscle strengthening exercise for older people can reduce the *risk* factors of falls, and thus may reduce the rate of falls. An increase in physical activity is likely to have other benefits too. Professional support appears to be important in promoting exercise and adherence. Social support, convenience and leadership are important factors in the success of this approach.

2 Assessment of the safety of the home environment, and a range of interventions such as safety checks and modifications, have been shown to reduce the rate of falls. However, the level of improvement was not sustained unless the intervention was maintained, highlighting the importance of regular surveillance.

3 Suitable footwear (well-fitting, and thin soles) can improve balance and stability.

4 Dietary supplementation of vitamin D and calcium in high-risk people may prevent fractures.

5 Hip protectors are effective, though often unacceptable aesthetically.

Description of the project

The objectives of the project have been:

- to identify older people at risk of falling and by working with them on a weekly basis to build strength and confidence to reduce the incidence of falls and/or injuries suffered as the result of a fall;
- to investigate the viability of achieving this, using a community-based holistic approach involving professionals from all disciplines.

Full assessments of participants were made in their own homes before, immediately after, and three months after the programme. Each weekly session was held at a local NHS clinic and included exercises (led by an NHS physiotherapist), a talk on a related subject such as diet or medicines, and time for tea and biscuits and a chat. Transport was provided to and from the venue.

Note. Due to the small numbers involved and the limited timescale, the project only attempted to measure proxy variables, i.e. established risk factors for falls. At the conception of the project, it was hoped to replicate previous research (benefits of exercise – discussed in *Preventing falls and subsequent injuries in older people*). This would have required recruiting control groups of participants and acquiring sophisticated measuring equipment (for example, to measure muscle power very accurately). As the project had very limited resources it was agreed that it was not possible to fulfil all the demands of an academic approach. It was decided to build on established research by assuming that a specific exercise regime could improve muscle strength and balance. It was hoped to be able to demonstrate this improvement and any other changes in general health and well-being that might occur.

Supporting the project

In planning the programme the Action on Accidents sub-group felt that it was vital that this project should involve all sectors of community services (health, social services, environmental health, leisure services, voluntary groups) and represent all districts in Warwickshire. Consultation at the outset of the project endeavoured to ensure support and commitment during the pilot stage and would facilitate adapting the programme for standard services in the future.

So the first stage was to invite all potentially interested groups to a half-day workshop. At the workshop information and opinions on existing practice and initiatives around the county were exchanged. Reactions to the perceived need and concept of a falls programme were received. Delegates were invited to join a working group to actually set up the pilot programme.

Sixty professionals attended the workshop in November 1996. It was encouraging that the issue of falls among older people was already recognised as a serious problem and delegates were very receptive to considering methods of reducing falls and injuries. The concept of the falls programme was received enthusiastically though there were strong reservations about how such a service could be incorporated into standard services without a considerable injection of funds.

From the workshop a core group of around a dozen people volunteered to be members of the working party. A broad spectrum of professions and districts were represented, as the following membership list shows:

Community nurse manager	North Warwickshire NHS Trust
Research project officer	Warwickshire Health Authority
Geriatrician	South Warwickshire General Hospitals Trust
Community nurse visitor	Clarendon Lodge Practice
Head of occupational therapy services	South Warwickshire General Hospitals Trust
PA to group	Warwickshire Health Authority
Health science practitioner	Warwickshire Health Authority
Head of health promotion services	Rugby and South Warwickshire Health Promotion
Clinical leader (health visitors)	South Warwickshire Health Care Trust
Health promotion	South Warwickshire Health Promotion Service
Physiotherapy manager	George Eliot Hospital NHS Trust
Clinical leader (health visitors)	South Warwickshire Health Care Trust
Public health nurse	Warwickshire Health Authority

All members of the group have been very committed to the project which has required a great deal of work outside the regular meetings. This has *not* been a project where one or two people do all the work, and the rest just turn up to meetings! In addition, other professionals have been involved at various stages.

The first task for the working group was to agree a protocol for the programme. This would cover:

- selection criteria (target group)
- recruitment method
- assessments/measurements for evaluation purposes
- topics and format of information sessions
- exercise schedule.

The *selection criteria* for recruiting participants was based upon the following characteristics:

- male and female
- aged 70+
- at risk of falling (GPs assessment: could be had a fall previously, under certain medication, with certain medical conditions, etc.)
- considered fit enough for programme (GPs assessment).

But to exclude any with:
- dementia
- incontinence (not controlled)
- a recent serious fracture, and still under rehabilitation
- neurological disorders.

It was recognised that these criteria exclude many at risk of falls; and there are also valid reasons for including younger people. As this is a small pilot project it was agreed to deliberately target a narrow sector in the hope that a fairly homogeneous group could work well together and provide meaningful conclusions for the project.

Mindful of the needs of other 'at-risk' older people, a sister project in nursing homes to cater for the very frail and, in some cases, demented older people is also being established. This scheme will closely involve carers and relatives, to raise awareness of the value of gentle exercise and other aspects of falls prevention.

It is intended that the messages of the Falls Prevention Programme will be included in the training of all healthcare professionals and carers so that people with specific requirements such as those with Parkinson's Disease and stroke victims can also benefit from this approach.

From the outset this project was intended for primary care, and sessions were to be nurse-led and set in the community. As far as possible the programme was not to be thought of as a type of hospital therapy or clinic.

For the pilot study it was decided to enlist the support of three GP practices which already had district nurses or community nurse visitors with dedicated responsibility for older people. These practices would recruit participants for the project and the nursing staff would conduct assessments and organise the weekly sessions. In fact, they did much more than this and the success of the project has much to do with their enthusiasm and excellent relationship with participants.

Originally it was planned to set up three groups to run simultaneously in each district of Warwickshire (North, South and East). Unfortunately at the start of the project in September 1997, it was not possible to set up a group in the Eastern area. There was one group in the (rural) North and one in the South. A group started in the (urban) North in April 1998.

Each recruiting practice selected twelve to fifteen suitable candidates for the programme.

The selection was either made by the GPs or suggested by the nurses in the practice. Approval for all potential participants to take part had to be given by the GP, to be sure that each person was medically fit enough to join the programme. *This was as much for the health authority's benefit as for the participants, to ensure that we were insured against injuries.*

Patients were contacted by a personal letter from their GP explaining the purpose of the programme and suggesting that they might benefit from taking part. The letter told them that the (named) nurse would phone or visit them in a few days' time to see if they would like to get involved. Only one of the patients approached declined to take part, and this was for personal reasons.

During the subsequent home visit there was plenty of opportunity to discuss the programme and the pre-programme assessment took place. Each of these visits lasted at least an hour.

Exactly what to *assess and measure* and how, exercised the group for some considerable time. The main reason for collecting measurements before and after the programme was to provide some basis for comparison, and hence evaluation. The assessment was also a tool to find out more about the person and how the programme could help him or her. It also highlighted any other needs he or she may have. There was a real danger therefore that the assessment could attempt to do too many things and it took some time to achieve a consensus on what should be measured and how long the assessment should take.

Helpful advice on how to measure power, reaction time, and other mechanical abilities was given. These required fairly sophisticated equipment (which was not available to the project) and a controlled environment for measurement. Given that ambitions for academic research had been abandoned, most of the assessment was structured with a fairly qualitative approach. For example, a range of everyday movements such as rising from a chair, climbing steps, standing still, and standing on one leg was looked at. The participant was asked to indicate (using a scale such as 'not at all, with difficulty, easily') how they thought they coped with the task, then the assessor recorded her own assessment for the task. These measures were repeated after the programme, and again after three months. To allow comparisons, each participant was assessed by the same person on each occasion. This approach was simple to administer in the participants own home, and has proved to be very useful in assessing the person's health, ability to cope in their home surroundings, and to provide an indication of their mental health. Naturally, it is hoped that it will fulfil its purpose as an evaluation tool, too.

The following headings indicate the topics covered:

- physical status
- postural stability
- social conditions (whether lives alone, needs help, gets out)
- home environment
- personal (type of diet, companionship, whether smokes, etc.)
- medical status and medication

- attitudinal measures on falling (fear of falling, confidence in getting up after a fall, restrictions on daily living).

Most of the *topics selected for the information sessions* were chosen on the basis of established research on falls prevention. As there were ten sessions to fill, it was possible to expand into areas of general health and well-being too, so some additional topics were included. The full list of topics to be covered is as follows:

- the value of exercise, and the importance of maintaining exercise
- footcare and footwear
- safety indoors (including heating and hypothermia) and outdoors (including road safety)
- medical conditions and medicines, insomnia
- diet, dentistry
- information and services available
- the ageing process, physical and mental care, continence
- healthy lifestyle (roundup session).

An important backup for the information sessions was a comprehensive information pack put together for the project by South Warwickshire Health Promotion department. Each participant received a wallet containing leaflets and information sheets on a wide variety of subjects.

The head of occupational therapy at South Warwickshire NHS Trust and the head of physiotherapy services at North Warwickshire NHS Trust worked together to produce *a schedule of exercises* specifically for this programme. Collaboration between these two disciplines made sure that the exercises would not only improve the physical status of participants but would also help them to cope with activities at home.

A booklet was produced with matchstick men diagrams, and suggestions for the number of times an exercise should be repeated. Also included were instructions on how to get up after a fall. The booklets were not distributed until after the first session so that the physiotherapist had had an opportunity to demonstrate the exercises and discuss which ones could be safely attempted at home.

Each session included approximately 20 minutes of exercise, and was led by an NHS physiotherapist, to comply with NHS insurance requirements. Included in the exercise sessions would be discussion, demonstration, with participation where possible, of how to get up after a fall.

'Programmes' of schedules were issued to participants. As each area arranged their schedule independently, the talk headings were slightly different. The content of the talks was not standardised but did conform to earlier briefings. Each session lasted approximately $1\frac{1}{2}$ to 2 hours, and included:
- a 30-minute talk, demonstration or video
- 20–30 minutes' exercise
- 30 minutes for refreshments, discussion and socialising.

Summary of procedure to set up Pilot Falls Prevention Project

1 Agree protocol.

2 Develop recruitment and assessment procedures, exercise schedule, choose information topics, compile information pack.

3 Identify GP practices to take part, liaise with nurses/CNVs to provide documentation for GPs, produce assessment forms.

4 Book venues (NHS premises), speakers, transport (NHS minibuses with qualified attendants to collect and return participants). The 'home' NHS community trust took responsibility for all local administration.

5 Produce and print programme of events for participants.

6 Conduct pre-assessments.

7 Commence ten-week programme.

8 Conduct post-assessment.

9 Conduct three-month assessment.

10 Evaluate project.

Funding

This project was funded by an award of £9000 from Warwickshire's Health of the Nation Fund to run a pilot project of an integrated ten-week community-based programme in three locations for older people identified as being at risk of falling.

The project has not been fully costed yet but first indications are that each of the three programmes have cost approximately £2000 to £2500 to implement. The cost of providing door-to-door transport accounted for more than half of this amount, and the remainder was principally nursing and the physiotherapist's time.

Fortunately the organisers of the programme and outside speakers did not charge for their time. Venues were provided free of charge, otherwise the setting-up costs would have added significantly to the overall cost of the project.

The cost per participant of providing this service would therefore be approximately £200.

Evaluation

The evaluation process is not yet complete, but is taking the following form:

• Comparison of pre-, post-, and three-month assessments
• Observation at some of the sessions

- Questionnaire and discussion with participants
- Frequent feedback from staff involved
- Informal focus group with staff involved.

Three elements are being considered:

- Procedure
- Financial
- Effectiveness.

Procedure

Setting protocol

This process was achieved with two or three meetings, plus circulation of consultation documents in between. Although this was a lengthy process, it allowed sufficient opportunity to explore as many potential problems as possible. The wide consultation at each stage ensured full support for the decisions made, which has allowed the pilot to proceed with confidence.

Identifying GP practices

In each of the three Warwickshire areas (North, South and East), GP practices that were known to already have an active interest in the well-being of their older patients in that they employed district nurses (DNs) or community nurse visitors (CNVs) with specific responsibilities for this age group, were approached. The first approach was usually to the nurse at the practice, and this was followed up with a letter to the senior partner at the practice. This letter described the project and outlined the level of commitment from the practice which at minimum would be to recruit participants, but ideally to involve the nursing staff at the practice in the assessments and weekly sessions. Reimbursement for staff time was offered. The letter was signed by a senior member of the public health department at Warwickshire Health Authority who is a member of the working group and of Action on Accidents.

Full co-operation and support was received from practices in the North and South, but due to unforeseen circumstances it was not possible to establish a group in the Eastern area within the timescale. It was agreed that two groups would proceed, and the third would be arranged later in the year.

Recruitment

Recommendation to the programme came from either the patient's GP, or the nurse who was already in regular contact with the patient. The GP approved all recommendations as being fit to complete the programme.

As described earlier, patients were contacted by letter from their GP then visited by their DN or CNV. Five men and nineteen women, aged between 77 and 91, were recruited.

This system of recruitment worked extremely well:

- There was confidence that each had been assessed by the GP *as being at risk of falling*. This is probably a better selection criteria than setting definitive categories such as 'had a fall in the last week/month/?', 'poor eyesight', 'dizzy spells', etc.
- By asking the GP to confirm (in writing) that the patient was medically fit to take part in the programme, protected his/her safety, and ensured that this responsibility stayed with the GP.
- Patients responded well to a personal letter from their GP, and were reassured that the programme would be safe and properly constructed. In most cases, participants already knew and trusted their DN or CNV, so they were easily convinced of the benefits of taking part. Most were virtually housebound and quite lonely, so they looked forward to the prospect of a weekly outing.

Assessment

Each pre- and post-programme assessment was conducted by the practice DN or CNV, the same person conducting assessments for each participant. The first assessment took about an hour, and subsequent assessments slightly less. Although there was a lot to cover, staff found that the assessments were easy to complete, and gave them the opportunity to get to know the participants. Participants enjoyed the visit, and appreciated that someone was taking such an interest in them.

Assessments were also an opportunity to highlight any problems (medical or social) that had not already been known.

Venue

Each area arranged to hire a suitable room at a local NHS clinic for the programme sessions. These naturally had easy access for disabled participants, plenty of suitable seating and refreshment facilities. Many participants were already familiar with the premises used, visiting them for chiropody or other therapy.

Although a 'clinical' atmosphere was not promoted, it was reassuring to be meeting in an NHS setting, knowing that all safety standards would be in place. It was also free!

Transport

Transport was offered to all participants, and most took up this offer – especially as the programme took place in winter. NHS ambulance minibuses with qualified attendants were provided, and the DNs or CNVs also accompanied participants. Although participants lived fairly near the venue, each round trip took at least three-quarters of an hour. Many participants were quite frail, and needed help to get from their home to the bus and on and off the bus. It was important to have several people available to help people from the bus into the venue.

Participants did not appear to mind the time spent 'on the bus', it became part of the outing, though it extended the session quite significantly for staff.

As noted in the funding section, transport was easily the most expensive element of the programme.

Information sessions

As previously described, some sessions were led by nurses, and others by outside speakers. Apart from one speaker, all were employed within health or social services. All speakers gave their time free of charge.

There were advantages and disadvantages to both ways of arranging speakers:

Outside speakers

Advantages:	Expert advice
	Variety
	No preparation for staff
Disadvantages:	Time-consuming to arrange
	Vulnerable to cancellation
	Less control on content (and length) of talk
	May be difficult to organise on a regular basis

Internal speakers

Advantages:	Familiar with audience
	More control on content of talk
	Can be repeated for another group
	Consistency
	Flexible
Disadvantages:	May not have sufficient expertise on certain subjects (e.g. interaction of medicines)
	Staff may not feel comfortable about giving talks
	Preparation time.

The benefits of having most talks prepared and delivered by staff probably outweigh the advantage of outside speakers in that it would be easier to guarantee consistency at all venues. Once the initial preparation had been completed, little extra work would be required at subsequent sessions.

It might be possible to enlist expert help to prepare talks on subjects such as chiropody and medicine, though there is no substitute for having an expert present to answer questions. On balance, it will probably be ideal to include some outside speakers but for most sessions to be led by staff.

Exercise

The booklet of exercises that was produced for this programme was the basis of all the exercise sessions at each location. This provided continuity, although the physiotherapist at each location could adapt the exercises according to the abilities of individual participants. Exercises were performed to light classical music at one location. This was enjoyed by participants and helped to maintain rhythm.

All participants took part in the exercise sessions, and it was clear that these were enjoyed. They were encouraged to repeat the exercises at home several times a week. Providing the booklet of exercises to use at home was invaluable. All claimed to exercise at home, every day in some cases. Perhaps some of these claims were slightly exaggerated, but most appeared to be genuine from the way they spoke about the experience. In particular, they did the exercises *because they felt better for doing them*.

To comply with NHS insurance regulations, the exercise sessions had to be led by NHS staff. District nurses and community nurses are usually employed by GP practices, and therefore are not covered by NHS employee indemnity. Our view is that with suitable training, these exercises do not require a highly qualified physiotherapist to lead them at every session. However, the issue of liability would need to be resolved.

Refreshments

The DNs and CNVs provided and prepared refreshments. At several sessions, participants brought home-made cakes or other treats. A 'party' was provided for the last sessions, which were held just before Christmas.

The social session was perhaps the most valuable part of the programme. Mostly it was just a time to chat and get to know each other, but there was also a chance to talk about the exercises or talks informally.

Effectiveness

Two programmes were completed in December 1997, and the third started in April 1998, so a full evaluation is not completed. Early signs are all positive with participants and staff indicating enjoyment of the programme and believing it to have real value.

Participants repeated the exercises at home, and there are strong indications that they will continue with them – *because they can feel benefits in terms of greater flexibility, less pain and improved balance*.

The value of providing an opportunity for socialising to an essentially housebound group, most of whom lived alone, was self-evident.

Recognition of, and interest in, the programme has also helped to raise awareness generally of the magnitude and seriousness of the problem of falls in older people.

A full analysis has not been made of the *Pre- and Post-assessments* but the main evaluation of the effectiveness observations so far are:

- At least half showed an improvement in balance.
- Two or three could now climb stairs (albeit slowly), which they had been unable to do before.
- A little more confidence shown about getting up if a fall should occur.
- Blood pressure had reduced for just over half of participants (this could be coincidental).
- All were happier and more confident in general than at the first assessment (assessors' appraisal).
- One lady ventured out into the village on her own, something she had not done for a long time (see quote at end of report).
- One was now taking her medicines more regularly, having followed the advice of the pharmacist and bought a medicine dispenser.
- Many remarked at the second assessment that they were continuing with the exercises as they could feel the benefit of them.
- Typical comments were 'They [the exercises] warm me up', 'I'm more flexible now', 'My shoulders are less painful', 'My walking is better'.

Staff at the sessions could see that participation in the exercises improved during the course of the programme. The ability to complete certain exercises improved, and the number of repetitions also increased. The 'fitter' members of the group felt that they could have attempted more vigorous exercise, but enjoyed taking part, nevertheless. The second assessments indicated that all were continuing with the exercises, whether this is still the case after three months remains to be seen.

All staff involved agreed that all participants had benefited greatly from the social element of the programme. Most participants lived alone, and could not go out without help. Several seemed very lonely at the first assessment. All very much enjoyed an opportunity to meet other people like themselves, and appreciated the 'nurturing' element of the project. The last session was rather sad, since all of the group would have loved to continue. Friendships that had been made were going to be difficult to sustain without outside help for transport.

It is difficult to assess the value of the information sessions. Once again, the sessions were found interesting, and participants were attentive and appreciative. However, when asked at the end of the programme what they felt the main message of each of the sessions was, they were struggling to recall anything very specific! As all the talks were backed up with literature, it is hoped that the information could be referred to when necessary.

The only topic that would not be repeated will be the session on continence. With hindsight this was a rather ambitious subject to introduce to a mixed sex group of this age range. The topic might better be addressed during assessment.

Perhaps participants did not fully grasp that exercise could directly reduce their risk of falling. They did believe that it was good for them, and in some cases were pleasantly surprised to find that they could actually take part in exercise. As they all claimed to feel the benefit, and intended to continue, it probably does not matter what their motivation is!

Long-term success

The success of the project will be judged on the following:

- Follow-up assessments of participants.
- Qualitative evaluation of the effects of the programme.
- Cost-benefit analysis: cost of prevention approach such as the Falls Programme v. cost of treatment and rehabilitation of falls. This will try to take account of the 'risk of falling'. For example, for the cost of treating one fractured femur (£5000 in-patient costs), twenty-five people at risk could attend a ten-week programme. Can it be assumed that the programme could prevent one of them from suffering a similar injury within one year? If so, then the cost of implementing the programme would be justified.
- Adoption of the principles of this approach into standard practice of all professionals in contact with older people.

Training issues

This pilot project has relied heavily on the professionals involved in the project, so there have been few opportunities for training so far.

It is intended to encourage this holistic approach to falls prevention to be adopted, or adapted, by all professionals. This will require training for many different groups of people: professionals training their own colleagues, but making sure that carers (professional and relatives) are also trained.

There will be significant opportunities for the health promotion services to develop training for non-professionals involved with caring for older people. (It is assumed that professionals will inform and train their own colleagues.) The next task of the project is to develop ways of adapting this approach to benefit a larger group of people.

Main outcomes to date

- Participants and staff are very positive about the programme. Benefits to the general well-being of participants have been self-evident.
- The programme has depended very heavily on co-operation from GP practices.
- Involvement with the programme triggered off other initiatives.

Other initiatives inspired by the falls prevention programme

- Falls Prevention Programme in nursing homes.

Funding has been awarded from Health of the Nation monies to set up a similar programme in four nursing homes. This project will recognise the importance of training and involving carers in falls prevention. It is hoped that the lessons learnt from this study can be easily adopted by other nursing homes. Early signs are that nursing homes are enthusiastic about this approach.

- Exercise training included as part of hospital discharge procedure at South Warwickshire Hospital.
- Community auxiliary nurses being trained in falls prevention in North Warwickshire.
- Links with over-75 primary care assessments.
- Links with project to establish home safety checks in Warwickshire.
- Links with Care and Repair and Alarm System Services.
- Links with Ageing Well: peer group educational visits may be initiated and Ageing Well co-ordinator is to contact participants (via CNVs and DNs) to invite them to the Ageing Well exercise classes.
- Recognition and interest from other organisations outside Warwickshire has raised the profile of falls prevention work.

Future plans

Future plans for the Falls Prevention Programme cannot be made until the pilot is complete and the project fully evaluated. It is unrealistic to expect that it will be possible to 'roll out' the service in its present form to all at risk of falls in Warwickshire, but it is hoped to influence current practice and adapt the programme for more general accessibility. For example, a 'programme' might be introduced in established groups such as sheltered housing, luncheon clubs and other associations, thus avoiding transport costs.

Finally

The following quotes from the assessors talking about some of the participants at the second assessment *(initials have been changed)* perhaps best sum up what we are trying to achieve:

'G has kept up with the exercises following the programme, and now feels physically stronger and more confident about getting up after a fall. She has taken note of several ideas from the information pack: she now eats breakfast every day, has a room thermometer, and keeps a sturdy chair in the room to help her up if she should fall.'

'F appeared to be a very lonely lady when I did the first assessment, she has really benefited from meeting and making new friends.'

'E doesn't use her walking stick as much now, as her mobility and balance have improved.'

'C feels that the exercises keep her supple and warm her up.'

'M has managed to go out alone into the village with her walking frame for the first time in many months, and is very proud of this achievement.'

Literature review

Sattin, R.W. (1997) Preventing injurious falls. *Lancet* **349**: 150.

Morgan, P. S. A. and Carter, Y. H. (1996) *A Study of Accidents among Older People in the UK.* RoSPA.

De Laet, D. E. D. H., van Hout, B. A., Burger, A., Hofman, A. and Pols, H. A. P. (1997) Bone density and risk of hip fracture in men and women: cross sectional analysis. *BMJ* **315**: 221–5.

Skelton, D. A., Young, A., Greig, C. A. and Malbut, K. E. (1995) Effects of resistance training on strength, power and selected functional abilities of women aged 75 and older. *JAGS* **43**: 1081–7.

Skelton, D. A., Greig, C. A., Davies, J. M. and Young, A. (1994) Strength, power and related functional ability of healthy people aged 65–89 years. *Age and Ageing* **23**: 3711–7.

Skelton, D. A. and McLaughlin, A.W. (1996) Training functional ability in old age. *Physiotherapy* **82**(3).

Torgerson, D. J., Garton, M. J. and Reid, D. M. (1993) Falling and perimenopausal women. *Age and Ageing* **22**: 59–64.

Sobczak, J. (1997) Music and movement to exercise older people. *Nursing Times* **93**(15).

Nuffield Institute for Health, University of Leeds (1996) Preventing falls and subsequent injury in older people. *Effective Health Care* **2**(4).

Health Survey of England 1996 (1997) Department of Health.

Main contact

Mrs Hazel Wright
Public Health Nurse
Public Health Department
Warwickshire Health Authority
Westgate House
Market Street
Warwick CV34 DE

Tel: 01926 493491
Fax: 019226 495074
e-mail: gen.office@warwick-ha.wmids.nhs.uk

North Thames

'Full of Beans': empowering older people and preventing accidents through promoting physical activity in Hertfordshire local authorities

Categories: Service Provision; Education and Training; Strategic Approach; Research

Start date: 1996
Completion date: ongoing

Executive summary

Existing methods of most accident prevention programmes have been 'top down' professional advice – passing on the advice perceived as appropriate for the age and the stage of the person being addressed. Traditional approaches to accident prevention assume that accidents are a primary cause of ill health among older people. Professional judgement led the consortium to believe that accident prevention is being delivered to older people on an age-based premise rather than a person-based premise. Advice that is given tends to be predominantly environmental, 'move that rug' or similar being perceived as an effective prevention measure. It is however too simplistic and this approach does not take into account the previous knowledge and experiences of the recipients or their wish to remain in control and retain independence. Nor does it give older people the knowledge and skills to do this.

Learning from literature searches that were commissioned, the research from this project demonstrated to the consortium organisers where traditional accident prevention methods fail in gaining commitment from older people. The project started in accident prevention and finished in the field of mental health and well-being but does still support the overall accident prevention work. 'Full of Beans' has been developed with a broad-based approach.

The traditional approach model to preventing accidents has been widened to place health issues in context. An empowerment approach has been adopted which addresses how to make use of older people's knowledge, and improve their confidence and self-esteem and at the same time offer skills and information which will maintain and improve their abilities and address some of the key priorities identified by this group. The project is primarily an exercise and relaxation programme for older people living in sheltered housing schemes. It has been designed to be delivered by warden care staff employed by local authorities and in the private sector.

Background

The Environmental Health Training Consortium has experience of working together on accident prevention projects for older people for over five years (Safety Backdrop Project/ Olive's List) 'Full of Beans' was developed in response to needs identified by evaluation of these earlier projects. The evaluation showed that *accident prevention was not perceived as a main priority by older people* and that advice given on accident prevention did not generally acknowledge this or take into account previous life experiences of older people. Primarily four issues were identified as priorities for older people:

- health and quality of life
- money worries
- stress
- retaining independence.

In addition, older people feared that an accident could be a major cause of loss of independence and mobility. Research also indicated a degree of social isolation and marginalisation for this group.

Advice on accident prevention can be predominantly grouped into two categories: 'move that rug or you will trip' or, a more recent development of fitting safety devices, door locks, etc., mirroring practices used with parents and children. Traditional approaches to accident prevention initiatives appear to be met with indifference and even hostility, and a sustained lack of measurable success in reducing injury or death in this age group, even though health professionals seemingly are held in high regard by older people. However advice can be viewed often by older people as interfering, patronising or unnecessary.

The Training Consortium was also aware of the more current research that demonstrated links between improved well-being and physical exercise but wanted to see if underlying benefits in reduction of accident rates for older people could also be identified, so it was decided to commission in 1996, a literature search 'on recent studies related to physical exercise for health gain with the elderly and any subsequent reduction in accident rates'.

The literature search showed that anyone at any age can make beneficial improvements through regular exercise programmes which can improve grip strength, balance, bone density and large muscle strength. All of these factors can be represented in accidents particularly falls. For example:

- A study undertaken in the USA by Stanford University showed that a 12-week regular exercise programme for older people improved thigh muscle strength by 25 per cent.

This could be the difference between getting out of a chair unaided and not.

- Similar improvements in hand grip strength can make the difference between falling badly and saving oneself from a fall.
- Exercise programmes need to include a number of components, for example muscle strength, suppleness and flexibility to improve reach and balance; stamina to improve the

cardiovascular system which can benefit such conditions as high blood pressure and diabetes; a social element which assists in maintaining regular attendance.

- A regular exercise programme can reduce stress and anxiety and improve short-term memory.
- Improvements in sleeping patterns and bowel function are also noted.

The conclusions are that traditional approaches to accident prevention assume that accidents are a primary cause of ill health among older people. Yet there are are complex factors involved in accidents which will vary with individuals while some can be addressed by making use of older people's knowledge. By adopting an empowerment approach, the skills and knowledge of older individuals can be enhanced and this can in turn improve abilities and take into account some of the priorities identified by older people. A physical activity exercise and relaxation programme can address a number of these priorities.

Another literature search was undertaken to look for references to work undertaken 'to assess the relationship between age-related stress and improvements that could be linked with regular use of relaxation techniques including alternative therapies'.

The findings from this research can best be described as being much less successful than the one done on exercise in identifying the benefits of relaxation techniques for older people. Although it is widely described in the literature, it is not age-related. It is also noticeable that stress among older people is not generally acknowledged in the literature. This was also confirmed as a general problem in anecdotal evidence obtained from local people who were consulted in Hertfordshire.

However 1 in 6 of the population will experience mental health problems at some point in their lives (according to MIND) and there is no particular reason why this should not be so after the age of 65. It is estimated that: 10–20 per cent of older people suffer from depression; 2–4 per cent more severely; and up to 60 per cent suffer from raised blood pressure.

Six trials have demonstrated that the effects of high blood pressure can be reduced by treatment that involves the mind as well as the body.

- Relaxation can reduce the stress response and so reduce the heart rate, blood pressure, breathing rate, muscle tension, state of mental arousal and adrenalin flow.
- Relaxation can reduce fatigue, gain deeper body awareness leading to better judgement about the amount of body effort to do everyday tasks, therefore reducing excessive and unnecessary tension.
- Relaxation can promote sleep.
- Relaxation can improve self-awareness, self-control, and the ability to cope and self-confidence.

Alternative therapies are also seen as having an effective role though it is impossible at present to separate the therapy from the attention and care of the therapist in order to determine the origin of the perceived benefits. It was therefore concluded that the benefits of physical exercise and relaxation are well enough documented among the general population for it to be considered an appropriate part of the 'Full of Beans' programme. Evaluation of the relaxation element will, however, need consideration at some stage.

Population

The total population of the three local authorities is 326,180 (Census data 1981) with approximately 19 per cent of the population being over 65 years of age. Those being targeted in the project fall between 65 and 94 years of age.

Description of the project

The project has been based in sheltered housing schemes in the local authority and private sector. It has been undertaken in three local authority areas, East Hertfordshire, Welwyn Hatfield, and St Albans City and District which cover a land area of approximately two-thirds of Hertfordshire and comprise both rural and urban settings.

The aims of the project are to develop a skills-based exercise and relaxation training programme which can be delivered by warden care staff employed in local authorities and the private sector. The objectives are to:

- enable staff with no previous experience to deliver a safe and suitable programme of exercise and relaxation to tenants in their care
- sustain a programme of this kind with minimum cost implications
- give access to exercise and relaxation to individuals previously unable to do so
- enable older people to recognise the benefits of regular attendance in maintaining independence, through improved suppleness, strength and stamina
- improve knowledge amongst older people that exercise can relieve depression, reduce anxiety and stress and improve self-confidence and self-esteem.

It consists of:
- a gentle exercise programme using a wide range of existing established materials, developed by a consultant with extensive experience with this age group;
- a relaxation programme based on well-tried muscle relaxation principles developed originally for the Health Education Authority's former Look After Your Self programme and amended suitably for the age group;
- a teaching and training programme developed for the warden care staff in order that they would be able to run an exercise and relaxation class in their sheltered housing scheme in a safe and suitable manner. An experienced trainer used to working with older people delivers this element.

Training

Unit one of the training pack of materials for the exercise for older people was developed so that the entire programme is fully documented and can be repeated or replicated by others. It is advocated that all elements should be used and that they should not be amended without consultation with a trainer who is qualified in the field of exercise.

The format

- Warden care staff have 3 x 2-hour sessions of skills training and teaching practice plus a 2-hour masterclass taken by an experienced exercise teacher who specialises in working with older people.
- Wardens are then visited as they start their programme with tenants.
- Charts of exercises and a full description are provided.
- Wardens are brought together after 8–12 weeks to discuss their progress with the trainer.
- Wardens are encouraged to support each other and fill in for illness etc.

The training programme is split into a number of sections:

1 Pre-reading for warden care staff. *Over 50 and All to Play For* (Sports Council) and a specially written document on the physiology of ageing.
2 The aims, outcomes, benefits and safety issues when running a class.
3 Health issues that could affect performance in an older age group exercise programme.
4 Health profile and GP permission form before a resident attends a class.
5 Running a class – structure and timing.
6 Session plan and purpose of each element.
7 Individual exercises illustrated and explained with alternative positions for standing supported and sitting.
8 Skills needed to teach an exercise programme.
9 Evaluation and quiz for warden participants in training.
10 Residents complete an evaluation form before they start a course and after 8–12 weeks.

Unit two of the training comprises the relaxation element, and the format for warden training in teaching relaxation techniques is identical to that used for the exercise programme and is based on the established methods developed for the Look After Your Self programme.

The programme is split into a number of different sections:

1 Pre-course study.
2 Health profile and GP letter for permission before resident attends a class.
3 Why relaxation is so important.
4 Aims and outcomes of a relaxation programme.
5 Outline programme, sessions 1, 2 and 3.
6 Health issues.
7 Neuro-muscular relaxation programme – setting the scene.
8 Signs and symptoms of stress.
9 Stress reduction strategies.
10 Teaching materials – individual exercises illustrated and explained.
11 Course evaluation forms for the warden training.

Supporting the project

'Full of Beans' is a multi-agency project and involves the statutory, private sector and the community. It has also involved older people in its development. The partners are: from *St Albans City and District Council* – environmental services health promotion manager and the housing and corporate policies officer; from *Welwyn Hatfield Council* – environmental services environmental health education officer and the social services community care manager; and from *East Hertfordshire Council* – environmental services environmental health promotion officer; *Stort Valley Housing* (East Herts); *University of the Third Age* (Welwyn Hatfield). A freelance consultant and trainer is employed to deliver the physical activity training.

The development team comprises the three officers from environmental health and the other local authority personnel.

Funding

The project has been pump-primed by Hertfordshire Health Agency and match funded in officer time and resources

Costs £3600 – spent on:

- literature searches – physical exercise and relaxation
- design and printing costs for literature searches
- consultant time
- trainer for warden care staff training courses
- design and printing costs for training packs
- 'Full of Beans' Unit 1: Exercise for older people
            Unit 2 Relaxation for older people.

Evaluation

The process has entailed:

1 Regular management team meetings to obtain feedback from all participants
2 Ongoing individual manager/warden evaluation of progress which has enabled any problems or queries to be addressed quickly and fed back into the management team. Alterations to the project have been undertaken based on this information.
3 Monitoring attendance patterns of participants as an outcome.
4 Self-evaluation of progress judged by participants – a subjective measure. As participants are 'healthy' older people in their judgement, medical methods of evaluation were not judged as suitable and could have been perceived as intrusive for a voluntary and recreational activity.
5 One-to-one feedback to support above – much information was gleaned in informal conversation.
6 Regular meetings with consultant trainer.

Evaluation outcomes

- Warden care managers have set up and maintained weekly exercise classes and have been able to incorporate the relaxation training at a later stage when this became available.
- Attendance by participants has been regular and sustained.
- Participants have identified benefits of regular participation: 'I can put my hat on'.
- Observed improvements have been noted by the warden: 'She is walking better and more confidently'.
- Improved physical confidence among participants.

Additional outcomes identified among warden care staff have been:

- Sustained interest and commitment to this way of working with residents.
- Identified benefits to their competencies to undertake their working role – the relaxation component was particularly identified as being both beneficial personally and in a one-to-one situation when residents were anxious or stressed.

Organisational outcomes

- Manager confidence and commitment to the process identified by the project.
- Changes in working methods to maintain the process among the warden care team by alterations to their job descriptions.

Negative outcomes

Various lessons have been learnt, among them:

- The inability to sustain schemes and commitment in all the areas that were piloted. This was due to major organisational changes and high stress levels in the organisation at the time, which reduced the ability to implement and cope with changes in working methods.
- However a year on these problems are mostly resolved and it is expected that the project will be repeated and should be more successful.

The three most important outcomes

- Warden care staff in their professional role can acquire the confidence and skills to deliver a safe and suitable programme of physical exercise and relaxation to residents in their care.
- Professional working practice can be changed in this setting to incorporate this as part of social care provision ('Full of Beans' activities are considered to fall into Category B Provision – Social Care under the Housing Benefit regulations which allocates the workload of care staff).
- The programme once in place can be sustained at low cost.

Recommendations

1 All care staff should receive training to deliver this type of programme. It can increase skills in line with NVQ competencies and could be part of the Carer Qualifications.

2 Working practices should be changed so that it is a regular and consistent part of care work with older people.

3 Benefits of regular exercise and relaxation to the 50+ age groups should be part of a national campaign over the next ten years.

4 Commissioners of contracts with care agencies should include requirements for this type of work to be undertaken regularly and to an agreed standard.

Main contact

Representing the Environmental Health Training Consortium – the health promotion staff of East Hertfordshire, Welwyn Hatfield and St Albans City and District Councils.

Mrs Evelyn Tyler
Environmental Health Promotion Officer
East Hertfordshire District Council
Wallfields
Pegs Lane
Hertford SG13 8EQ

Tel: 01279 655261 ext.400
Fax: 01992 55280

Accident prevention for older people in Islington – a training resource

Categories: Strategic; Training and Education

Start date: June 1992
Completion date: Ongoing

Executive summary

The Accident Prevention and Older People Pack was developed to enable older people to have access to information on how to improve their health and avoid unwanted risks. The information is presented as fact sheets that give basic information and resource sheets that inform people of resources available in the local area. The subjects covered include improving health, using the health service, preventing falls, safety with medicines as well as safety in the home, garden and on the street. The pack has been translated into five community languages (Bengali, Cantonese, Greek, Gujerati and Turkish) because the black and minority ethnic communities make up about 20 per cent of the resident population in Islington.

The project has taken the form of a community-based intersectoral approach with shared responsibilities between individuals and a wide range of statutory and voluntary organisations. It also has incorporated existing work and resources and looked at environmental changes that automatically protect people.

Background

Healthy Islington is a multi-sectoral agency established in 1989 to make improvements in the health of people who live and work in Islington. It is supported by Camden and Islington Health Authority, Islington Council, University of North London and voluntary organisations in Islington. Its work is based on the framework of World Health Organization's (WHO) Health For All principles of community participation, multi-sectoral collaboration and addressing inequalities in health.

The work programme centres around three key areas of accident prevention: equity and access, health promotion and health protection. It has a strategic role in policy development and its main strength has been the development of a wide range of new initiatives and projects and the encouragement of other agencies to participate in the steering of such work. Other areas of work include needs assessment, research and information, training and national and international networking.

Healthy Islington established accident prevention as one of the key areas of its work because of the high accident rate in Islington. The five-year average annual death rate due to accidents in Camden and Islington is 40 deaths per year for men and 20 deaths per year for women (per 100,000 population; OPCS 1988–1992, *Camden and Islington Public Health Report, 1993*); which is much higher than the national average for men (27) and women (17). Over the period 1979 to 1983, Camden and Islington ranked the sixth highest boroughs in the country for deaths due to 'external causes', the vast majority of which are accidental (DH 19, *Mortality and Geography*, 1979–83).

Although accidents affect all age groups, older people are particularly vulnerable and have more accidents. The age-specific death rates for accidents, 1988 to 1992 in Camden and Islington in persons aged 65+ was 54.4 compared with 8.8 in children under 15 years and 17.2 in persons aged 15 to 34 (per 100,000 population; PHCDS, 1993, based on OPCS data).

In the UK, it is estimated that about 4600 older people die each year and 500,000 require hospital attention each year as a result of accidents. They also account for overall costs through treatment of injury and occupation of a high proportion of hospital beds. Falls comprise about 65 per cent of all accidents to older people for which hospital treatment is sought.

Supporting the project

In August 1990, a multi-agency group (called the Accident Prevention Group for Older People) was set up to initiate and co-ordinate work on safety and older people. The group consisted of representatives from:

Islington Age Concern; Islington Pensioners' Forum; Islington Council (road safety, social services, trading standards, special services team, race equality unit); Islington Community Health Council; District Health Authority (health promotion, occupational therapists, community pharmacists and physiotherapists); British Gas; London Electricity; London Fire Brigade and St Pancras Housing Care and Repair

Description of project

It aims to:

- raise awareness by providing accurate, up-to-date information on accident prevention work with older people for use by workers and older people
- empower older people through training and development work to make informed choices about modifying their behaviour and attitude to safe practices

- provide information and/or access to means to prevent accidents in the home (for example where to get smoke alarms and other safety equipment).

At the first two meetings of the accident advisory group, it was clear that a lot of information on accident prevention work with older people was already available, but widely dispersed and not readily accessible. The group therefore decided to collate the information available into an accessible format and turn it into a resource pack.

To ensure the widest possible uptake of the resource pack, it was decided to target it at groups and professionals who work with older people and to translate it into the five community languages widely spoken in the borough.

A wide range of other statutory, non-statutory, voluntary groups and older people were consulted (through meetings and correspondence) and contributed to the contents and its production. The process of consultation and production of the pack lasted a year and the pack was launched in September 1991 by Jeremy Corbyn MP at the Islington Town Hall.

There are ten sections in the resource pack covering subjects which include: improving health, using the health service, preventing falls, safety with medicines as well as safety in the home, garden and on the streets. Each section has a fact sheet that details basic information on the subject and a resource sheet with information on resources available in the local area.

It is designed to be used by workers who have a responsibility for accident prevention work with older people. It can also be used by older people themselves or by their carers. It can be used in a number of different ways:

- as an information and resource directory for workers seeking a range of information about accident prevention work with older people
- as a means of identifying suitable professionals when planning accident prevention workshops
- as a networking resource
- as a training resource for workers.

Target group

The project is targeted at older people aged 65+, who make up over one-fifth of the population in Islington.

Training

The main initiatives contained in the training programme included:

- awareness-raising skills on accident prevention for targeted professionals and older people
- facilitation skills training for workers to enable them to run accident prevention sessions either for older people or for their colleagues (cascade training)

- joint multi-professional workshops and seminars on accident prevention.

Training on accident prevention has been carried out in about 35 day, health and community centres with workers and older people. The training days for older people were held separately from those with the professionals. Although the sessions were similar, additional issues were covered in the sessions with the workers. These included basic approaches and opportunities in accident prevention, collecting information about accidents, conducting a safety audit of premises and working with others (materials and network support available in Camden and Islington).

The training with the black and minority ethnic groups was also slightly different. This took the form of cascade training with workers and some older people who could speak English fluently, so that they were able to raise the awareness of other older people in their communities. The packs have been translated into five community languages (Bengali, Cantonese, Greek, Gujerati and Turkish) and they have been widely distributed.

Each session took the form of a short presentation briefly describing the accident prevention programme and examples of local initiatives relating to older people. This was then followed by a half-hour view of two videos on how to prevent fires and accidents in the home and outside on the streets. The purpose was to highlight: the types of accidents that older people are usually involved in; the natural changes that occur as one gets older; how to make necessary adjustments to such changes; and ways in which accidents can be prevented.

Since 1991, about 10 accident prevention workshops and seminars have also been held. These were aimed at the different professionals who work with older people and or have an interest in accident prevention work. The aims of the workshops were to share information and good practice of work, opportunities for networking, and explore possibilities of joint initiatives that could be developed. The workshops were designed to encourage broad-based participatory discussion sessions, to ensure that participants recognised the very broad range of factors and issues involved in accident prevention.

In-house follow-up sessions were also offered to community groups, organisations and GP practices in order to provide support that matches needs and interests in the different settings. This was mainly targeted at GP practice staff and other primary healthcare professionals because of the advantage of their frequent contact with the population. The project has also led to other new project developments, but activities and involvement from the primary care sector have been low.

Four pieces of in-house work have been completed with City and Islington College, Islington Age Concern and Roman Way Medical Centre. Activities carried out included providing information, consultancy support and training to staff with a particular focus on safety audit and safe premises.

Training for older people was held separately from those with the professionals. Several workshops and seminars on accident prevention have also been held. These workshops attracted primary healthcare staff, staff from social services, trading standards, British Gas, local educational institutions and community workers. These have resulted in three in-house training sessions with staff, to match the needs of different settings and to carry out the audit of the premises.

Evaluation

The resource packs were widely distributed together with questionnaires to determine how local groups and professionals were approaching accident prevention work with older people and to identify their training requirements.

At the same time, consultation with the black and minority ethnic communities took place (lasted three months) to determine how they would like the resource pack presented. The issues that emerged from this study were used to inform the training programme.

Evaluation of the pack and the training has been ongoing. The training sessions were eval-uated by obtaining comments after the sessions. In general, participants revealed that the sessions were very useful. In particular, the feedback from older people was very encourag-ing. Many of them commented that the sessions challenged some of their unsafe practices and that they would now be enabled to make informed choices (rather than have it forced upon them) about modifying their behaviour and attitudes to safe practices.

Many also revealed that they come across some problems in trying to avoid accidents because of the design of living accommodation and other appliances in the home (for example, ignition points of gas ovens placed at the back thus making it more difficult to light). They also made other suggestions and requests for support and practical help with the purchase of safety equipment, for example, smoke alarms.

Community workers and other professionals also commented that the sessions would enable them to review as well as incorporate issues of safety into their working practices. They commented that the workshops were particularly good ways of identifying opportu-nities for joint action, liaison and support.

Funding

The project has been funded through various sources.

In the first year of operation (1990/91), it was funded through Joint Finance and a part-time worker was appointed to co-ordinate the production of the pack.

In 1991/92, a secondment (for six months) from environmental services joined the team, with the responsibility of organising the launch and distribution of the pack as well as iden-tifing an overall strategy to carry the work forward.

In 1992/93 through the Inner-City Partnership Fund, a freelance health educator was appointed to carry out the training identified within the strategy. Other freelance health educators have also been used for the training and the workshops and seminars held. These and the reprints of the pack have been funded by monies received from Camden and Islington Family Health Services Authority.

Since 1990, the estimated cost of the project is about £50,000. Healthy Islington co-ordinates the work of the group which meets four times a year.

Outcomes

Many of the suggestions and issues raised in the feedback sessions have been passed on to the relevant sectors and agencies. They have resulted in constructive changes being made to services offered to older people and other new developments. These include:

- Extending the time at crossings (2–3 seconds longer) to give more time for older people to get across.
- Stopping Occupational Health from charging older people for aids less than £20.
- 'Let's Get Alarmed' project which installed smoke alarms on an estate and organised door-to-door distribution and fitting of smoke alarms to all households on low income (by Camden and Islington Health Authority).
- The Home from Hospital Scheme (from the Whittington Hospital) which provides short-term support to older people after discharge from hospital. The support is provided by volunteers who encourage them to keep fit and active by taking them to day centres where they can participate in a number of activities.
- A training pack on accident prevention for use by GP practice staff and other primary healthcare professionals has been developed.
- Joint work – strategically, this work with older people has provided a forum to which many organisations and various sectors have contributed. It has also served as a focus for other developmental work and project bids in the district. Examples are the Islington Accident Prevention Alliance (set up by the Health Authority as part of the Health of the Nation strategy); Islington Health Action Plan; and the Health Action Zone bid which is part of the Health Improvement Programme and Health Strategy.
- Undertaking two amended reprints of the pack.
- Changes have been made to the format of the training.
- Enabling working practices to be reviewed within services on offer to older people in a constructive way as well as challenging some of the unsafe practices by older people.

Presently a review is being conducted by the Accident Prevention Group for Older People to update the pack and training programme as well as look at alternative ways of approaching primary care services.

Future plans

Feedback from all the people involved in the project showed that the work has been of great value. Although reduction in the number of accidents occurring is difficult to determine in terms of the activities generated, the good practice disseminated, and new project developments, it has been of immense benefit. It also showed the significance of working intersectorally and its links with different organisations are a cost-effective way of working.

A review of the programme is now being conducted with Manor Gardens Centre, Islington Age Concern, Islington Carers' Forum, Islington Pensioners' Forum and the district health authority. The aim is to look at the possibility of developing a long-term strategy based on the resource pack and the training, and to develop a funding package as well as decide the best sector or agency to take a lead role in the work.

The accident advisory group will look at expanding the languages into which the pack is currently translated. This is because the proportion of black and minority ethnic older people is rapidly increasing due to a significant international migration of asylum seekers, and refugees in the 1990s.

Exploring other methods of involving GP practice staff and other primary care professionals in this work because of their little involvement in the programme to date will also be pursued.

Main Contact

Monika Schwartz
Co-ordinator, Healthy Islington
159 Upper Street
London N1 1RE

Tel: 0171 477 3035
Fax: 0171 477 3029
e-mail: healthyislin@dial.pipex.com

South Thames

The focus on falls project in Worthing

Categories:

Service Provision   developing a model for service provision
developing screening tools
developing interventions to reduce risk

Research   profile of population (fallers aged 70+)
and Audit   identification of patterns of risk and associated interventions
outcomes of interventions

Education   health promotion educational material suitable for fallers, manual
for staff and associated training

Start date: December 1996
Completion date: March 1998 but possibly extended to November 1998

Executive summary

The project is based in a GP surgery covering two group fund-holding practices and takes a pro-active approach to fall prevention and risk management for older fallers in the community. It is aimed at developing and evaluating a model for service delivery in primary care with a view to enabling community staff to provide a more focused and comprehensive service to fallers.

Information about fallers has been gathered. Health education material on risk reduction has been produced. Although the project has not been designed to obtain evidence of effectiveness some outcome indicators have been used to gain information which will be useful in directing future research.

The project has yet to be evaluated. Early findings indicate that fall prevention requires additional expertise to that of the average experienced healthcare practitioner who may have only a partial view of the problem. Some useful tools and methods have been developed.

Clients who have fallen and hurt themselves have been relatively easy to identify and a proportion of this group requires intervention to reduce the risk of subsequent falls. However, it has proved difficult to find clients who have fallen without hurting themselves.

Background

This initiative was developed in response to Health of the Nation targets. The Worthing area has one of the highest populations of older people in England and consequently there are a large number of falls in the area, many of which result in fractures of the neck of the femur. The multiple causes of falls are now well researched and understood. There is some evidence of effectiveness for interventions to reduce risk. There is, however, a gap between research-based studies and actual application in practice.

Research into fall prevention was initiated by West Sussex Health Authority. A part-time researcher was appointed for one year (July 1995–June 1996) to review current literature on causes of falls and identify evidence-based techniques of fall prevention and risk management.

As a result of this work a successful bid was made to the Department of Health Community Care Development Programme for funding for a two-year primary care project for people aged 70 years or over who have already fallen. The partners in the bid were:

- West Sussex Health Authority
- Worthing Priority Care NHS Trust
- West Sussex Social Services.

The structure of the service and its objectives were developed by the researcher, a senior research occupational therapist, in discussion with others. The aim is to reduce incidence of falls, and especially of fractures of the femur, a long-term aim to which the project will contribute.

The main objectives have been to:

- increase awareness of fall risks and risk reduction methods among older people, their carers and professionals
- identify risk and reduce the risk for individuals who have fallen
- improve the 'managing' strategies for individuals at risk of falling.

Description of work

The project has four elements as indicated:

1 Intervention with the target population in the community
   This is aimed at risk identification and reduction and interventions include:

- exercise
- home safety check with removal of hazards and provision of adaptive equipment or safety aids
- lifestyle advice
- education in coping/managing skills and strategies
- modification of risk-taking behaviours.

2 Health promotion

For and with older people and their carers, with specific attention to fall prevention and risk management. Identification of material to support this, and development of additional information if required.

3 Staff development

Improving awareness of risk assessment and risk management. Development of training materials.

4 Information

Covering audit and evaluation.

It should be noted that a separate Department of Health project is reviewing links between medication and falls.

In undertaking this project there is a falls team which comprises a senior occupational therapist and a senior physiotherapist who were appointed in December 1996. Each works 12 hours a week for the project.

Older people are referred into the project through written referrals from participating doctors, district nurses, community physiotherapists or occupational therapists, scheme managers (wardens of sheltered housing), Home Care, day hospital, Littlehampton Minor Injuries Unit and the Worthing Accident and Emergency (A&E) Department.

The A & E department staff identify patients who are 70 years and over attending hospital following a fall and are registered with the participating practices. The notes on these patients are reserved and a clerical assistant calls once or twice a week to collect the details and forward these to the falls team.

Screening interview

Clients referred from the A & E department are assumed to have differing levels of need. It is impractical to offer a home visit to all fallers. Screening is therefore conducted by means of a telephone interview. This differentiates the fit, active, coping group from those who feel vulnerable following the fall or who have risk factors which require intervention.

On receipt of the notification from A & E, the client is sent a letter to alert him or her that someone will telephone. The RoSPA leaflet 'Falls, how to avoid them and how to cope' and the Health Education Authority 'How you can be more active' leaflets are included, together with the falls team contact number in case further advice is required.

A member of the team then telephones the client and conducts the screening interview. The questions are focused on identifying people with a past history of falls, decreased mobility, reduced independence, expressed need for more help and increased concern over falling. The client is also asked if a visit is wanted.

At the end of the interview, primary and secondary risk factors are counted. The presence of any of the primary risk factors is taken as a signal for the need for a risk assessment home visit. Anyone for whom the situation is unclear, or expressing a wish to be visited is also offered an appointment. Those with no risk factors may be sent additional information such as a leaflet on the Lifeline call system and are urged to contact the team if they become concerned about falling, or fall again.

The risk factors included in the screening tool are selected from research evidence as being predictive of falls and also being practical as telephone questions. Although it should follow that increased risk increases the probability of falling, the tool is not being used to predict falls since the project is not structured to ascertain whether or not falls subsequently occurred. The tool is used to discriminate only between clients who need a risk assessment home visit and those who do not.

In order to validate the reliability of this tool, it is being evaluated by randomly allocated visits to people judged not to need one. These visits have to date confirmed that these clients do not have unmet needs or unrecognised risk factors requiring intervention. More detailed formal research will be needed to confirm the predictive validity of this tool with different populations and to confirm interrelated reliability.

Home visits

During the home visit a detailed fall history interview is conducted together with a screening check for home hazards and presence or absence of safety equipment. Consequences of the fall are investigated and coping strategies for any future fall are explored.

The fall history interview is designed to obtain information on the client's personal situation, the circumstances and consequences of the recent fall, effectiveness of coping strategies and level of concern over falling. Questions on health and lifestyle are also asked. Structured observations of the client's cognitive function, vision, communication skills are made during the interview.

A risk rating based on personal independence is instrumental (domestic and household activities) together with available resources for undertaking these tasks. (The Assessment of Living Skills and Resources (ALSAR) has been developed in America by Williams et al. (1991).)

The Up and Go is used to assess mobility. (This test is adapted from the 'timed up and go' test (TUAG) developed by Podsialo and Richardson (1991) and the 'get and go' test developed by Mathias et al. (1986).)

On the basis of this information the presence or absence of 16 risk factors is ascertained. When a risk factor is found it is noted and an outline action plan to deal with it is negotiated with the client. Further assessments are conducted subsequently if required.

Throughout the interview the team member endeavours to follow the client's agenda and to respect personal needs and wishes. Intervention is only provided after full discussion and with the agreement of the client.

Interventions

For clients having a number of risk factors, or requiring specific treatment, an intervention plan was agreed and carried out in the home.

For each risk factor there is a summary of the assumptions on which intervention is based, cross-referenced to available evidence, rated on an alphanumeric scale of reliability.

The assessments, interventions and outcome measure (where available) are also detailed.

Interventions typically include one or more of the following elements:

- a personalised exercise programme
- advice on personal independence
- advice on coping strategies in case of a fall
- advice on removal of home hazards and provision of safety aids

or referral to other providers. Advice to carers is also given when needed.

This work is ongoing, but production of a manual is planned which will act as a basis for training, service provision and the further development and evaluation of techniques.

Health promotion material

Existing material (for example, RoSPA leaflets; HEA Active for Life materials) are used and materials are being produced (see 'Outcomes' below).

Population

The two group GP practices have a combined population of 5984 people aged 65 and over. Statistics on the incidence of injurious falls suggested that about 2000 fallers aged 70+ might be expected within this population in the course of a year, of whom 200+ might be injured sufficiently to seek medical attention.

Funding

The total funding for 22 months is £70,000 which has included development of publications, data collection and evaluation.

The running costs for the team, travel, accommodation, etc. has taken about £30,000 per annum.

Evaluation

Detailed analysis of information gained from the project is under way and will be published during 1998. This is being undertaken by the audit department of Worthing Priority Care NHS Trust with help from the health authority research department. Forms used to collect factual information about fallers have been designed to be scanned. Data are analysed using the SPSS programme (a statistical programme).

The project has focused on service development. Whilst some evidence of effectiveness may be obtained it will not be possible, without further research, to give reliable evidence of whether the project has been successful in reducing falls.

It will be possible to provide a detailed profile of the client group, details of prevalence of risks, details of what interventions were carried out in relation to each risk, and any measurable outcome (broadly interpreted as evidence of risk reduction due to intervention).

Training

Training for healthcare professionals will be developed in time, but this is likely to take until the end of 1998. Training will be aimed at enabling people to use the screening tool, conduct home assessment visits using the procedure and tools developed by the team, and at improving the quality and consistency of strategies used to reduce risk and improve coping skills.

Outcomes

During the project the falls team (occupational therapist and physiotherapist) have developed a screening tool for fallers referred by the accident and emergency department, a procedure for a risk assessment home visit and evidence-based assessments and interventions for specific risk factors.

- The level of referrals indicates that it has been possible to find people who have fallen and injured themselves, a proportion of whom require intervention. It has not proved possible to find people who have begun to fall, but have not yet injured themselves. The difficulty in finding this important target group is a matter of concern.
- As a result of the home visits 50 per cent of clients were found to have problems which could be dealt with rapidly (after the first or one subsequent visit) either by the team or by referral to another agency.
- The falls team is developing a manual for local use for healthcare professionals on evidence-based practice to guide interventions. Each risk factor has a section.
- A pack of basic A5 leaflets for local use is in production. Titles include:
  - 'Take care, be falls aware' (a cognitive behavioural approach to risk reduction)
  - 'Drugs and falls'
  - 'Home hazard check' (a simple, quick one for client or assessor to use)
  - *Trips, slips and falls: Prevention and Management in Residential and Nursing Care: a Guide to Good Practice* (booklet for home managers and staff)
  - *Stay on Your Feet*: an adaptation of an Australian book for older people giving more detailed advice on fall prevention. This will be published (with permission) as a set of leaflets for use with higher-risk clients.

Recommendations

As the project has not been completed it is not at the stage to make recommendations. To date, results of the project have been influenced by local circumstances and the characteristics of the sample population which is not, on the whole, affected by financial, social or environmental deprivation. This makes it necessary to be cautious about how far project findings and procedures can be generalised at this stage.

Initial findings indicate that:

- Referral via accident and emergency departments identifies a high proportion (75 per cent +) of injured fallers who need advice or help.
- Screening is a valuable and practical way of targeting services to those most in need.
- For anxious or less mobile people exercise may be better conducted in groups initially, then followed up at home.
- Education of professionals about fall risks, risk management and coping strategies needs to be improved and extended to ensure a comprehensive approach.

It does seem that further work is needed to find effective systems for risk reduction in community settings and to provide evidence of effectiveness for these measures.

References

Mathias, S., Nayak, U. S. L. and Isaacs, B. (1986). Balance in Elderly Patients: The 'Get up and go' test. *Archives of Physical Medicine and Rehabilitation* **67**: 387–9.

Polsialo, D. and Richardson, S. (1991). The timed 'Up and go': a test of basic functional mobility for frail elderly persons. *Journal of the American Geriatric Society* **39**(2): 142–8.

Williams, J., Drinka, T., Greenberg, J., Farrell-Holtan, J., Eurardy, R. and Shram, P. (1991). Development and testing of the Assessment of Living Skills and Resources in elderly community-dwelling veterans. *Gerontologist* **31**(1): 84–91.

Main contacts

Rosemary Hagedorn, DipCOT, DipTCDHEd., MSc., Project Co-ordinator
Or:
Deborah Russell, MCSP and Sara McLafferty, DipCOT, Falls Team

Until November 1998:	*After November 1998:*
Willow Green Surgery	Head of Occupational Therapy Services
Station Road	Occupational Therapy Department
East Preston	Southlands Hospital,
West Sussex BN16 3AH	Shoreham-by-Sea EN43 6TQ
Tel: 01903 859180	Tel: 01273 455622
	Fax: 01273 446075

Anglia and Oxford

The Elderly Persons' Integrated Care System (EPICS) in Marlow

Category: Service Provision

Start date: 1994 and ongoing

Executive summary

The Elderly Persons' Integrated Care System (EPICS) in Marlow, Buckinghamshire, aims to support people in the community by providing flexible, responsive packages of care according to assessed needs, placing particular emphasis on speedy responses to prevent inappropriate admissions to hospital in times of crisis. EPICS aims to:

- provide easily accessible information.
- provide a single point of access 24 hours a day.
- co-ordinate assessment to ensure the best possible package of support for clients and carers, and most importantly:
  - to provide at short notice an EPICS care worker with a flexible package of short or out-of-hours visiting, overnight and 24-hour support.

Description of work

The Marlow EPICS is an integrated care and support system available to any person of 65 or over, registered with a participating GP practice, to ensure the most appropriate use of health and social services and community resources, in order to optimise their care within legal, budgetary and resource constraints.

The aims being to optimise choice for users and carers and to provide a co-ordinated care and support network.

Historically, the care of the older person has revolved around institutions resulting in care that is organisationally orientated, rather than client focused. Evidence suggests that older people prefer to remain in their own homes and communities for as long as possible. Community care planning has moved a long way in developing community services, but generally they are unable to react quickly enough when a crisis occurs, other than in the form of an ambulance/A & E response. This results frequently in inappropriate admissions to hospital and delays due to discharging difficulties. Hospital can be the most dangerous place for an older person to be!

Demographics demonstrate an increasing need due not only to an ageing population, but also ageing carers, more people living alone and 'increased reliance on community resources at times of health and social service budget squeezes.

National policies are recognising the current issues of increasing need and addressing them by realigning allocation of resources. Increasing importance is being given to primary care provision and the need for properly co-ordinated and collaborative working. Pilot schemes such as EPICS are essential to provide the basis for evidence-based proactive care to be developed.

The EPICS Board, involves representation from NHS Management Executive, GP fund-holders/purchasers, social services, Bucks Health Authority, voluntary sector, plus user and carer representatives. User and carer representatives feature at all levels of management, as well as service provision levels. The Board is responsible for policy making and securing resources,

The service is based at Marlow Health Centre and available 24 hours a day, 365 days a year. Access to the service being provided by Marlow Community Hospital at night and district nurses over the weekend.

Once a call is received, a phone call/visit is made to the client/carer for an initial assess-ment. EPICS care worker home support team provides 24-hour rapid response to 63 per cent of all referrals to this service. For example, this may be a 24-hour presence, night attendance, a series of check visits throughout the day, or helping the client in or out of bed. The average length of intervention is 7.5 days. The co-ordinator will also collaborate with other providers such as social services, to arrange whatever other support may be nec-essary. The EPICS care worker support, therefore, gives the other services time to under-take assessment and put in place their own service support. Once referred, the client then has one point of contact from which their care package will be developed. Volunteer ser-vices can provide longer-term support as required.

EPICS is underpinned by IT systems tailor-made to provide an easily accessible client data-base, resource database and monitoring facilities. The client database holds essential infor-mation on all residents of Marlow aged 65 and over. It is updated regularly with information on admissions and deaths received directly from hospitals, A & E and GP prac-tices. It is accessible only by password to EPICS staff, but provides key information to GPs/district nurses/social workers on enquiry if dealing with a new referral.

A directory of services and amenities is also available to ensure that the resources of the community are known and can be targeted to individual clients. This can save GPs and other practitioners hours of frustration and duplication and provide the users and carers with information and choice.

The Geographic Information System software identifies clients on a street map, which can then be overlaid with information on community resources, statutory services and infor-mal support networks. The potential for integrated planning across health and social services is yet to be developed. The client population size of this project is approximately 3500 registered with their local GP practice in Marlow.

Funding

The project development was supported by joint finance funding for five years, tapering to health and is now mainstream through the trust's directorate of elderly care services. A special grant was obtained from the Department of Health for IT development. Other funding was provided through a once-only opportunity of a ward closure.

Approximately £52,000 is provided to manage the scheme, including the salaries of one full-time co-ordinator, one full-time equivalent for clerical and data input, one part-time data supervisor. Also nine care workers are contracted to the service plus auxilliary bank nurses are paid hourly on-call rates to provide 24-hour, 365-days-a-year cover.

Evaluation

The need to demonstrate to the purchasing authority that the project had a cost benefit in saved hospital bed-days drove the first attempt at quantitative evaluation.

Clinical audit

An audit of over 65s admissions to hospital within the trust of patients registered with Marlow GP practice was undertaken over a five-month period. A set of criteria was developed to enable the clinical audit teams and the clinicians to determine where EPICS, if mobilised, could have helped prevent admission where not clinically necessary, and facilitated early discharge. The audit findings suggested that 564 bed-days could have been saved by referral to EPICS. In the five-month period, after allowing for the costs of EPICS input, just under £220,000 could be saved and redirected to other services.

Consumer satisfaction survey

A consumer satisfaction survey was carried out by an independent interviewer using critical incident technique methodology. Thirty of the 109 clients referred to EPICS were interviewed in the same five months as the audit was carried out, and a high degree of satisfaction was recorded. Particularly valued was the immediacy of the response, the flexibility of the service to meet their needs, the reliability and ease of access. The follow-up by a volunteer phone link was also highly rated.

A GP satisfaction survey

A GP satisfaction survey was also carried out independently over the same period, again with very positive responses. Twenty-two out of a possible 24 forms were returned and 12 out of 15 GPs said that EPICS intervention had prevented admission to hospital. The 24-

hour access reliability and swift response were especially valued, giving the GPs peace of mind over the safety of their patients and giving them time on co-ordinating community or other services. – 'Happy patient, happy doctor'.

Marlow EPICS was quoted as a model of best practice in integrated care in the Audit Commissions Report *Coming of Age* Oct 1997.

Training

All stakeholders, including volunteers, have been involved in a series of whole-day work-shops. Training is essential to the development of integrated pathways to understand one another's boundaries. To develop solutions to problems and realise opportunities, it is essential to understand how systems interact with one another.

Trainers from America came in to provide the initial four days intensive training with funding supplied from joint finance and a local commercial company.

Regular training for volunteer teams and care workers is undertaken and there is an annual review of practice and performance by practitioners, managers, volunteers and users.

Outcome

- Immense savings in hospital bed-days could be saved due to timely crisis intervention.
- 70 per cent of clients and carers preferred EPICS intervention.
- 87 per cent of referrers said the EPICS intervention was appropriate and timely.

Future plans

- The scheme is being rolled out to another area in Buckinghamshire (Amersham/ Chesham).
- Development of Internet and geographical information systems.
- Community-based prevention programme on falls.

EPICS is only one of the initiatives in southern Buckinghamshire being developed and supported by the Older Persons Accident Focus Group.

Members of the group include:

Regular members:
- Wycombe District Council (WDC)
- South Bucks District Council (SBDC)
- Chiltern District Council (CDC)
- Social services – direct care service
- Bucks County Council – road safety
- Bucks County Council – fire and rescue service
- ROSPA – regional area officer

- NHS – A & E consultant
- NHS – community staff nurse
- Bucks Health Authority (BHA) Health For All co-ordinator
- Bucks Disability Information Network
- EPICS
- Anchor Housing
- UK Asian Women's conference

Receiving minutes and contributing as necessary
- Thames Valley Police
- Bucks County Council – trading standards
- Social Services – care manager
- Bucks Age Concern
- Beacon Housing Association

Contact

Mrs Christine Stanners
EPICS
Marlow Health Centre
Glade Road
Marlow
SL7 IDJ
Buckinghamshire

Tel/Fax: 01628 476789

South and West

Promoting positive health for older people: 75+ check schemes in Wiltshire

Category: Education, Training and Resource

Start date: June 1995 and ongoing

Executive summary

With the introduction of the 1990 GP contract came annual health assessments for the over 75s. A review of these assessments in Wiltshire identified health promotion as a key area for development. Wiltshire Health Authority Primary Care Support Unit convened a group of practice nurse mentors and a health promotion specialist to develop a health pack to include information sheets, assessment protocols and an exercise tape and leaflet to be used by health professionals when conducting 75+ health checks. The pack concentrates on six key areas: blood pressure, continence, mental health, accident prevention, mobility and exercise, and healthy eating.

Description of initiative

Four practice nurse mentors, each specialising in a particular discipline, a primary care facilitator and a health promotion specialist having an exercise speciality, developed laminated assessment sheets in the five areas. The pack contains individual information sheets on using annual assessment cards, blood pressure, continence, mental health, accident prevention, helping people change, mobility and exercise, as well as an exercise leaflet and tape.

The information in the pack recognises the interlinking health concerns between issues.

- The section on mobility and exercise addresses issues, causes and checks for preventing falls.
- The section on accident prevention looks at the environmental factors as well as safety and falls.
- The cards indicate a course of action following an individual's response to the questions.
- There are prompt cards and on the reverse is a checklist.

The pack is aimed at health professionals, mainly doctors and nurses because it is suitable as a guide to be used with individual patients as well as having the basis of protocols for the primary healthcare team. The contents are also pertinent to those who work with older people. It can be used with carers and others to raise awareness of potential hazards.

Funding

The funding for the project was provided by the primary care support unit, with Wiltshire Health Authority also incorporating normal staff time.

The cost of producing 1000 packs was approximately £5000.

Outcome and future plans

- The packs were disseminated to GP practices throughout Wiltshire during December 1996.
- Following this dissemination it was decided that a comprehensive pack should be developed which included not only the laminated cards but also relevant information sheets and healthy eating information.
- Four afternoon seminars were held throughout the county in November 1997 and health professionals, link workers and representatives from social services attended.

  The packs are available to agencies outside Wiltshire, price £10. The exercise booklet and exercise tape can be purchased at £1.00 each.
- There are plans to undertake an evaluation in 1998.

Main contact

Kate Harris
Primary Care Support Unit
Wiltshire Health Authority
Southgate House
Pans Lane
Devizes
Wiltshire SN10 5EQ

Tel: 01380 728899

Doorstep Walks in Wiltshire

Category: Community Health Initiative

Start date: February 1996

Executive summary

Walking is an ideal gentle start-up for the sedentary, particularly for the older population. The initiative was originally developed to provide primary healthcare professionals with an alternative to the GP Exercise Referral Scheme. A pack of ten accessible local walks of between 20–65 minutes' duration has been produced.

Description

The packs can be used by primary healthcare professionals in consultations when encouraging patients to be more active on a regular basis. The packs have been designed to provide access to physical activity that was unsupervised, not facility-based and offered in a relatively unstructured way.

The packs have been disseminated at no charge to the general public through GP surgeries and health centres, libraries, social services departments and voluntary organisations.

Supporting the project

Salisbury Health Promotion, Salisbury District Council, Wiltshire County Council, SE Wiltshire Ramblers' Association and Wiltshire Wildlife Trust were involved in the development of the pack.

Funding

This initiative was funded by Salisbury Community Forum, the Health Education Authority (*Active For Life* local grant), Wiltshire Rural Action for the Environment and Wiltshire County Council Travelwise.

2000 packs were produced at a unit cost of 75p.

Evaluation

The walks were launched in March 1997 and an evaluation was carried out in October, 1997:

- 61 per cent of people requesting a pack indicated that they had used the Doorstep Walks pack.
- 87 per cent of the those walking stated that they were likely to continue with the walks
- 69 per cent said they were more likely to take exercise like Doorstep Walks rather than exercise at a leisure centre.
- 59.3 per cent of the walkers were over 50 years of age.

A report is available.

Future plans

In Wiltshire the initiative is being widened to other areas where there are already expressions of great interest from general practitioners in both rural and urban centres. These future initiatives will allow further and more detailed evaluations concentrating on the longer-term sustainability and impact of the scheme to be undertaken.

Main contact

Dawn Vernon
Wiltshire Health Promotion Service
Oak House
Greenways Centre
Malmesbury Road
Chippenham
Wiltshire SN15 5LN

Tel: 01249 454270
Fax: 01249 454271
e-mail: oak@chipoff.wilthp.btinternet.com

'Sit and be fit' training course across Wiltshire

Categories: Education and Training

Start date: February 1998 and ongoing

Executive summary

This 'Sit and be Fit' training course was developed by the health promotion service to provide a one-day course for staff working in residential homes and day care centres.

Background

The course was devised for several reasons. The health promotion service regularly received requests from residential homes for names of suitable tutors to run exercise classes though there were no funds to support such a project. In addition an initiative managed by Age Concern Wiltshire to provide exercise tuition in residential homes had been withdrawn as funding was no longer available.

Age Concern Wiltshire and Wiltshire Health Promotion Service were involved in the planning, organisation, delivery and evaluation of the course.

Description

Managed by Wiltshire County Council Social Services Department, attendance on the course enables participants to run simple and safe chair exercise sessions. Each course participant received a follow-up visit both to provide support and eradicate unsafe practice.

Evaluation

This will be carried out six months after the training course (September 1998).

Funding

Training venue £80
This costing is exclusive of staff time in health promotion which includes organisation, set up and evaluation time.

Interim outcomes

Organisers for a day centre in Devizes report a marked increase in mobility and personal confidence. The exercise regime, coupled with health promotion talks, has had substantial 'added value'. For example, many individuals who previously had tasks done for them have now taken on the running of the activities. This has freed up time for staff to attend to those in greatest need. Exercise has proved to be so popular that the day centre is planning to enter a 'musical exercise' display in the 1998 social services day centre autumn concert – rather than the traditional music only performance.

The chief officer of Age Concern Wiltshire has indicated that, although the trainees had previous experience and training, this training course has provided new routines and ideas, and eradicated some unsafe practices.

Main contact

Dawn Vernon
Wiltshire Health Promotion Service
Oak House
Greenways Centre
Malmesbury Road
Chippenham
Wiltshire SN15 5LN

Tel: 01249 454270
Fax: 01249 454271
e-mail: oak@chipoff.wilthp.btinternet.com

Home safety check and small repairs service in Chippenham

Category: Service provision and education and training

Start date: November 1996 and ongoing

Executive summary

The service has been planned and developed by a multi-agency and professionals' working group and was developed following a local research study. The service addresses the problems faced by older people which can cause accidents, in particular falls, and undertakes small jobs around the house.

Background

The idea for the project was conceived in 1995 but was not launched until late 1996. This initiative was developed from a research study completed on behalf of North Wiltshire District Council on home safety check schemes and the recognition by voluntary and statutory agencies of a high incidence of accidents in the home among older people. The research study was undertaken as part of work for an MSc by an environmental health officer undergraduate. The study considered a needs assessment for a home safety check scheme. It was directed towards health professionals and staff who work in a caring capacity. Additionally there was direct work undertaken with groups of older people.

Partnership support

The multi-agency involvement includes representatives from the Health Service (health visitors), the health promotion service, the county council social services department, North Wiltshire District Council (Environmental Health and Health Initiatives Department), the Council for Voluntary Service, Age Concern Wiltshire and Anchor Staying Put, North Wiltshire.

This group meets quarterly, acting as an advisory body.

Description of service

The service for both the home safety checks and the small repair scheme, which offers light repairs such as replacement of light bulbs, is managed by Anchor Staying Put and is based at their offices. The overall Staying Put service also deals with more extensive repairs and adaptations for people living in their own homes so there are occasions when there is an interchange of the small repair scheme and the larger scheme on offer. A technical officer who can advise the home safety check worker on various building matters is employed.

Funding

The service employs a worker for 29 hours a week and he uses his own vehicle.

The service costs around £22,000 per year and this has been raised from North Wiltshire District Council, JCT funding, and various charitable trusts including Allied Dunbar Staff Charitable Trust and the Chippenham Borough Lands Charity.

Evaluation

A questionnaire was devised and sent to the first 150 clients. This was done in conjunction with the health promotion service. The results show that the service has been well received by older people and is well targeted at those on low income, especially women living alone.

To continue the evaluation, questionnaires are now sent to one-in-ten new clients.

Outcomes

- Initially the small repairs service has appeared to be more popular than the Home Safety Check Scheme. The former seems to answer people's immediate needs.
- A wallet of leaflets has been produced to help to give the service more professional credibility. It includes publications from national organisations, for example, the Department of Trade and Industry and Help the Aged. The wallet that holds the leaflets was designed by Chippenham College and all clients now having a home safety check receive one.

Recommendations

- The right person is needed for the job which involves building up people's trust. Ideally the worker should have a basic knowledge of benefits and of what services are available locally, including services like window cleaners, decorators, gardeners, etc.
- It is useful if the service can be fitted into some kind of a management structure so that the worker gets the necessary support and administrative back-up.
- The Home Safety Check Scheme requires a stronger element of marketing and education in order to increase its uptake.
- Some kind of home safety check and prevention training is required.

Future plans

The plan is to continue the service, hoping that the financial support from the district council continues so that it can be used as a lever for obtaining the rest of the funding required.

Main contact

Nina Stimson
Anchor Staying Put North Wiltshire
3–4 New Road
Chippenham SN15 1EJ

Tel: 01249 460701
Fax: 01249 461440

Staywell 75+: volunteer visiting health-care scheme in a Cirencester general practice

Category: Research; Service Provision

Start date: 1986
Completion date: Ongoing

Executive summary

This has been an evolving project over a period of eleven years. Current practice for older people stems from earlier research in which trained volunteer visitors with health visitor support, were able to select and target focused assessment by the health visitor and other professional workers as well as provide social support in a cost effective way.

At the research piloting stage of the project a well-validated postal questionnaire was initially tested in the practice which has since been appropriately modified for the six partners working in a central surgery. It detects people of 75 years and over with a wide variety of self-perceived problems.

Because findings in the study and in further years confirmed that the majority (50 per cent and over) of people with an average age of 80 years were fully independent, the present system has changed and evolved until the present time when a two-phase anticipatory care (screening programme) is operational for all over 75-year-olds in the practice.

The practice is able to select and target in a more focused way their 75+ health check assessments through this scheme. The 24 volunteer workers are also helping to provide the social and befriending support to older patients in the practice in a cost effective way. They also elicit information on accidents experienced and can offer advice on accident prevention and identify those at risk from falls.

Background

In 1986 it was identified that whilst there was a well established service model for children there was an un-met need for support to be offered to older people in Gloucestershire. The work emanated from a controlled trial supported by a South West Region research grant from 1986 to 1989, from which the present anticipatory care model has developed. In this trial, a targeted health visitor review occurred in the intervention group after prior screening by trained lay visitors (volunteers). This focused review required a fifth of the health visitor contacts compared with a health visitor working in the standard way. Mortality was reduced with a more effective use of secondary care resources. The findings are fully described in the report *Stay Well 75+* available from the surgery and in publications.

The findings of this study and research in subsequent years found that over 50 per cent of people with an average age of 80 years had low disability and did not require long-term follow-up or annual review. This prompted a two-phase screening programme using a well validated postal questionnaire which had been piloted in general practice. Following its introduction, it was found to significantly reduce hospital admission and institutional care compared with a control group that was studied. The questionnaire is used following further piloting to detect people with a wide variety of self-perceived problems.

Description of work

It is the policy of the practice to offer an annual medical review to all patients over 75 years. Twenty-four trained volunteers see about two hundred patients in a structured visiting pattern dependent on a disability score using the Winchester Disability Score.

All patients not having a regular review in this way, by their trained lay visitor are invited to complete a comprehensive postal questionnaire developed by Professor John Pathy. Criteria have been developed to respond to this questionnaire (over 90 per cent completion) and selective response occurs by telephone or visit to those who identify problems interfering with their day-to-day living. Patients with continuing health or social problems are then introduced to the lay visitor structured visiting scheme in which regular surveillance and support is provided according to the disability score. Failed postal questionnaires are followed up by telephone or visit.

The overall aim of the scheme is to promote good health and well-being with registered patients aged 75 years and over, with the help of trained volunteer visitors. The main objectives are to:

- provide appropriate training and support for volunteer visitors and extend knowledge of age-related issues into the community;
- develop an early warning system enabling people to stay in their own homes in a dignified way for as long as possible;
- help alleviate patient problems associated with loneliness by encouraging volunteer befriending and developing a patient's support/social network;
- extend knowledge of local services and help available to patients via informed volunteer visitors;
- visit and initiate contact and to extend knowledge of services to all new patients aged over 75 years;
- implement a system of regular patient health reviews by incorporating information from a health questionnaire completed by a volunteer and patient in the patient's own home into the annual medical GP review;

- maximise effective use of support services;
- provide a system of referral to other agencies (professional or voluntary) after assessment of patient/client needs;
- provide a regular review system of assessment of patient disability levels for all people opting into the scheme;
- provide a selective system of health visitor professional assessment when appropriate, for example having a high disability score or specific problems.

Phase 1: Postal questionnaire system - patients aged 75 years and over - Surgery

Yearly postal questionnaire to patient ⟶ Analysis by HV
Annual invitation to patient for
medical review

Action by HV and
selective response by practice team

Selective referral to volunteer
visiting scheme

Phase 2: Staywell 75+ visiting scheme – selected patients 75 years and over

Invitation letter ⟶ Volunteer visits patient. Winchester
questionnaire. Advice on local services.
Invitation to annual medical review.

Analysis/scoring of questionnaire by HV and admin. assistant

Band Score Low Low/Med Med/High High

Revisit 12 months 6 months 3 months 3 months

HV action or home assessment for:
1. High score
2. Band change
3. Request from another agency
4. Volunteer support

High scores - Practice care plan after discussion by practice
team and external involved agencies.
Co-ordination and review by key worker.

Recruitment and support for the volunteers

Increasingly volunteers are recruited into the scheme from within the practice or directly from the local Volunteer Bureau. They are requested to commit themselves for a minimum of two years and on average stay for three years. They are trained and insurance for them is provided through the local Volunteer Bureau which also assists with external support. The volunteers are divided into two groups with team leaders who are trained and then meet regularly with the health visitor.

There is a quarterly meeting of the Staywell team, including the two team leaders, when the aims and objectives are reviewed in order to set future policy. There is an audit cycle and review of the whole system.

Population

Phoenix Surgery provides primary care services to about 10,000 people in Cirencester of whom about 650 are over 75 years of age.

Funding

The Staywell 75+ team consists of a health visitor employed by the practice for 20 hours per week contract from GMS budget with 70 per cent reimbursement. An administrative assistant is employed for ten hours a week from GMS with 70 per cent reimbursement.

The volunteer expenses, printing of questionnaires, day-to-day running costs are entirely supported from the Phoenix Surgery Charitable Trust and cost about £1000 per annum.

Anticipatory Staywell 75+ Team

The scheme is co-ordinated by the health visitor and supported by three-monthly review meetings of the group, consisting of Dr Beales, the HV, the administrative assistant, team leaders of the volunteer groups and the practice manager.

Training

An introductory training programme for volunteers, based upon the aims and objectives of the Staywell scheme, is spread over seven weeks consisting of seven 90-minute sessions organised in the autumn. After the training, each volunteer visitor should be:

- aware of the role of the volunteer visitor within the scheme;
- aware of the relationships between volunteer, client and professional;
- able to outline certain circumstances which may lead to stress in an older person's life;
- able to use some preliminary counselling skills;
- able to record information using the specified questionnaire;
- able to summon professional help and advice when needed;

- able to give some information on state and voluntary help available to older people.

Input to the training includes the GP who talks about the ageing process, an occupational therapist, social services and the health visitor/co-ordinator of the scheme. It also includes role-play and issues such as stress management.

The health visitor organises monthly group discussions with outside agencies as appropriate and volunteers join in on meetings held in the practice when there are outside speakers talking about relevant older people's health issues.

Evaluation

A 90 per cent response rate to the questionnaire was achieved at the pilot stage. No evaluation has been undertaken since 1989. There is some evidence of success from the GP contacts, visits and consultations with 95 per cent of questionnaires being returned and two-thirds of the target group apparently are healthy and living fulfilled lives.

Informal feedback from the patients indicates that they appreciate this befriending scheme.

Outcomes: the future

The scheme is a very structured model for the anticipatory care of older people, supporting the work of the health visitor. The screening programme is in full operation with a twenty-four lay workers as an extended arm of community care and has promoted the focused deployment of scarce professional resources.

There has been a halving of the general practitioner consultation and visiting rates for the over 75-year-old patients in the practice between 1986–89 (when complete figures are available from the original research project) and 1996–97. Comprehensive activity figures are available from the practice computer (Emis from 1991).

It is planned to continue with the scheme with the aid of development grants. It will look at the need of carers.

Contact

Liz Hicks
Health Visitor/Co-ordinator
or Dr David Beales
Phoenix Surgery
9 Chesterton Lane
Cirencester
Gloucestershire GL7 1XG

Tel: 01285 659235 (office)   01285 652056 (practice)
Fax: 01285 641562

The effect of a mobility programme on perceived distress and fear of falling among older people in Trowbridge

Category: Research - Pilot study

Start date: January 1996 and ongoing

Executive summary

This project was developed by the health promotion service to investigate the effect of a mobility programme within the primary care setting on the risk and fear of falling in older people.

Three mobility classes were set up, each lasting ten weeks led by a qualified EXTEND tutor. Referrals came from four primary health care teams in Trowbridge. A second cohort was also recruited from two residential and day care centres to form two further classes run from January to March 1998.

Population

Participants were identified using the following criteria:

- Men and women 65+
- Limited physical mobility
- Fear of falling
- Ability to self-complete a questionnaire
- Ability to stand unsupported.

Thirty people were referred into the scheme by their GP. A further 40 people were recruited through two residential homes with day care facilities.

Evaluation

Participants completed a health questionnaire at the beginning and end of the programme. Two validated tools were employed to assess the effect of the intervention – the Nottingham Health Profile (Hunt, Mckenna and McEwan, 1994) and the Fear of falling efficacy scale (Tinetti *et al.*, 1990).

Funding

This initiative has been funded by Wiltshire Health Promotion Service and costings cover the following:

Employment of EXTEND tutors	£1150
(60 classes of $1\frac{1}{2}$ hours plus planning and preparation time)	
Venue (mostly free of charge)	£100
Transport (provided by Red Cross for 2 classes)	£240
Total	£1490

This costing is exclusive of staff time from the health promotion service which includes organisation, set up and evaluation time.

Outcomes

Initial findings from the first cohort, although statistically inconclusive do indicate positive effects which can be summarised as follows:

- a reduction in levels of self-expressed fear of falling
- an increase in self-expressed physical mobility and ability to sleep well
- a decrease in self-expressed social isolation, pain and negative emotional reactions.

It should be noted that from the initial cohort of 30 people referred by their GP, 19 were unable to be included in the evaluation for the following reasons:

- selection criteria incorrectly applied
- data collection incomplete or
- dropped out prematurely for a variety of personal reasons.

The second cohort completed the programme in March 1998 and an evaluation report will be available in the summer (June/July 98).

Recommendation

More subjects are needed to draw any firm conclusions from the quantitative data.

References

Hunt, Mckenna and McEwan (1994) *Nottingham Health Profile* Revised Edition. Produced by Galen Research.

Tinetti, M. E., Richman, D. and Pavell, L. (1990) Falls efficacy as a measure of fear of falling. *Journal of Gerontology: Psychological Sciences* 45(6): 239–43

Main contact

Cathy Lees
Wiltshire Health Promotion Service
Oak House
Greenways Centre
Malmesbury Road
Chippenham
Wiltshire SN15 5LN

Tel: 01249 454270
Fax: 01249 454271
e-mail; oak@chipoff.wilthp.btinternet.com

General practice database on accidents in Ludgershall

Category: Research and Audit

Start date: April 1997
Completion date: April 2000

Executive summary

This project is looking to establish an accident data collection system for use within the primary healthcare setting in order to increase the level of local information available for targeting preventive action on accidents.

Background

The concept of the project was initiated and developed by Dr A. Greig who devised as a pilot, a data collection tool. This was initially as part of a one-year study and has been expanded to include five other practices in the area and the original tool modified to incorporate categories on socio-economic status and causality.

Description of the initiative

Data on all accidents presenting to a sample of general practice in the Salisbury area during the period April 1997–April 2000 are being collected. The A & E department of Salisbury District Hospital is involved in collecting similar information for patients of the practices involved and is collaborating on the systems being developed. The project is aiming to compare data from urban, rural and semi-rural practice populations as well as details on status and ethnicity.

Information collected includes such details as types of accidents, what afflicted them, what the patient was doing at the time, the type of injury, which part of the body was affected and what went wrong to cause the accident. The information allows for primary healthcare workers to discuss at practice meetings identified people at risk, causes, number of follow-ups and referrals. This can lead to more specific targeting and development of appropriate interventions to be undertaken.

Data are collected manually by practices on a specially designed card and these are collected and put on a database monthly by a data collection clerk employed by the project. The health promotion service is analysing the data on behalf of the project steering group, which is chaired by Dr Charles Holme, Consultant Community Paediatrician at Salisbury District Hospital.

Population

Data are collected on all accidents in all age groups presenting to the general practices but the system can be simply accessed by age groups, sexes and marital status, etc.

Funding

The Wiltshire Health Authority has provided £5000 p.a. for three years which enables a data collection clerk to be employed and covers other expenses such as travelling, administration, telephone and printing costs.

Intended outcomes

- Annual reports will be produced on data collected.
- A final project report will be written on completion.

Trends and priorities for accident prevention will be identified for use within individual practices and to inform practice across the county. Collecting data in a standardised format both in A & E and primary care is being aimed for.

Main contact

Dr A. Greig
Ludgershall Health Centre
Central Street
Ludgershall
Andover
Hants SP11 9RA

Tel: 01264 791500
Fax: 01264 790993
e-mail: roskoff@msn.com

'Handihelp' in West Wiltshire

Category: Service provision

Start date: April 1996
Completion date: Ongoing

Executive summary

A multi-agency partnership initiative which has commissioned a 'Handihelp' service from the voluntary sector to provide repairs, home security, home safety and *light* gardening for older people. Following a needs assessment, for identification of older people needing help with small jobs in the home, a local scheme was introduced.

Description of work

The work undertaken is simple, for example changing locks and replacing light bulbs. It was perceived that all referrals into the scheme would be directly from professionals as no direct advertising is undertaken. GP referrals are the norm but increasingly through word of mouth there are self-referrals.

The aim is to assist older or disabled people to maintain an independent life in their own homes with specific links to accident and crime prevention and improved housing conditions.

Background – needs and assessment

This project originated from a GP practice and the social services department leading to a joint health and social services approach to the assessment of older people's needs. It was undertaken through meetings and face-to-face consultation, for example comments from Trowbridge Older Persons' Group. Both users and carers have been involved during the consultation period and also through being part of the multi-partnership group to develop service specification. There is no specific proforma to questions posed but they are pursued through conversation with older people. This is an ongoing process.

Partnership support

This project is supported by multi-agencies and multi-professionals together with client groups to include the West Wiltshire Housing Services, Social Services (Inter-link Worker), Wiltshire Health Authority (Partnership Manager), general practitioner, West Wiltshire Community Safety Partnership, Carers' Network, West Wiltshire CVS and West Wiltshire Users' Group.

Project base

The project is managed within the local authority, West Wiltshire District Council Housing Services located in Trowbridge, serving the five towns and surrounding areas of West Wiltshire.

Population

The target group is people 65+ and also people registered as disabled.

Funding

Funds have been provided from Health and Social Services Joint Finances, Healthy Alliances (Health Authority); Local Authority Housing Services; General Practice and Social Services initiative funding as well as from community safety monies.

An initial £32,000 was provided from the above sources with a £11,000 recurring budget.

Evaluation

To date the scheme has not been evaluated although it is intended to do this through establishing whether the client has been satisfied with the work carried out.

Training

Training is being planned for home safety checks and bidding for additional training money is in hand.

Outcomes – future plans

The three most important outcomes learnt from the initiative to date are:

- older people can influence service delivery
- low level, preventive needs are important for older people
- multi-agency partnership working improves relationships *and* services for older people.

To sustain the project in the long term there are plans to:
- try and gain sponsorship from British Gas
- consider taking a small payment from older people.

Future plans include

- developing training packs for the Home Safety Check Scheme
- employment of a handiperson to carry out the three essential roles:
    (i) Handihelp
    (ii) home safety checks
    (iii) promotion of scheme (talks etc.).

Main contact

Lynn Gaskin
Social Services
Wiltshire County Council
County Hall – Eastwing
By the Sea Road
Trowbridge Wilts BA4 8J

Tel: 01225 773500
Fax: 01225 776096

The Avonsafe accident prevention alliance strategy 1997–2000

Category: Strategic Approach

Start date: April 1997
Completion date: April 2000

Executive summary

The 'Avonsafe – Action for Safety' strategy aims to reduce death and disability resulting from accidents in the most vulnerable groups in the population – in line with national targets. Avonsafe co-ordinates and generates accident prevention activities across the Avon area, involving as many individuals and organisations as possible whose work and interest includes accident prevention. Member organisations include health, local authorities, emergency services, and the voluntary and private sectors.

Description of the work

The foundations of the Avon Accident Prevention Alliance were laid down at the end of 1991 with the establishment of an advisory group whose main purpose was to review and promote accident prevention for people of all ages in Avon. The group continues to be a multi-disciplinary organisation supporting small sub-groups addressing the accident prevention needs of children, the 15–24 age group and older people.

The framework for joint working is well established, with an external evaluation of Avonsafe recognising the long-term commitment of partners to alliance working. The alliance has a policy of reviewing its aims every three years and the strategy discussed represents the results of the review.

The strategy is based on several key principles. These are that the strategy:

- seeks to address inequalities in health and promote access to accident prevention for all sectors of the community
- uses recognised accident prevention approaches, i.e. education, environmental modification and enforcement (approaches will often be combined)
- recognises and aims to complement other relevant strategies such as alcohol and physical activity. It also acknowledges the links between broader policy issues such as Local Agenda 21
- will be continually monitored and evaluated.

Key areas for action

The Avonsafe – Older people's group, which comprises twenty key member organisations, agreed the key areas for action for reducing accidents to older people.

Local accident statistics reflect national trends, which demonstrate that falls are the leading cause of death and injury among people aged over 65 years. The local priority is, therefore, to reduce the number of falls and subsequent injuries happening to older people. Research evidence suggests that the most effective accident prevention approaches should include education, improving the environment, and lobbying to make products safer, as well as laws that support prevention programmes. The plans outlining current work and proposed action are written using this recommended approach, and are concerned with primary and secondary interventions.

Population/age/gender

The sector of the population aged over 65 in the area covered by the strategy is estimated to be 161,000 people representing 16 per cent of the total population in the Avon area.

Funding

The alliance does not have a dedicated budget and the work of the alliance is funded by organisations pooling their resources and seeking sponsorship for activities. The strategy was funded by member organisations contributing to the cost of its production.

Evaluation

The strategy is used as a working document and is continually revisited at Avonsafe meetings. The strategy will be evaluated. Avonsafe produces an annual report, which will include monitoring data on accident trends, an account of how Avonsafe has worked as an alliance and details of Avonsafe interventions and outcomes. Avonsafe will systematically review areas for action; recording progress, identifying gaps and ensuring that appropriate action is taken.

Training

Avonsafe aims to provide high quality training opportunities, which are described in the strategy under 'Key areas for action'.

Outcomes

- A high profile strategy launch which included the signing of a 'Safety partnership charter' by top dignitaries and executives from 30 organisations across the Avon area reaffirmed commitment to Avonsafe.

- Where possible and appropriate, Avonsafe members strive to ensure that the strategy has support at the highest level from the organisation they represent. For example, it has been fully endorsed by Avon Health Authority and some local authority committees.
- The strategy is used by member organisations to develop operational plans.

Three years after publication (i.e. in April, 2000), Avonsafe will review the strategy and decide whether an updated version is required.

A limited number of strategies is available on request from the main contact person.

Contact

Maggie Sims Senior Health Promotion Specialist – Accident Prevention
Health Promotion Service Avon
Henshaw House
Cossham Hospital
Lodge Road
Kingswood
Bristol
BS15 ILF

Tel: 0117 975 8031
Fax: 0117 9750607
e-mail hpsa@netcomuk.co.uk

Accident prevention with older people in Romsey using information and training interventions

Category: Education

Start date: May 1997
Completion date: Ongoing

Executive summary

This project set out to develop work on accident prevention in a rural community.

A home check leaflet was written by a multi-agency group and distributed to adults visiting pharmacies for prescriptions during a four-week period. The leaflet was evaluated by district nurses with their patients and by pharmacists.

Training for carers and health professionals increased understanding of the causes of accidents and health professionals gained knowledge of effective interventions.

Further oportunities for work have arisen as a result of the training and the project will continue to develop.

Background

The Southampton and South-West Hampshire Health Authority has a multi-agency strategy for the prevention of accidents for people aged over 65 years. It has been in existence since July 1995 and is reviewed annually.

Each year, Southampton and South-West Hampshire Health Authority together with other agencies involved, identify priority areas of work for the coming year.

In 1997, the locality of Romsey was chosen to be used for some interactive interventions. Two settings were chosen – primary care and the community.

Romsey is one of four local authority areas in the catchment of Southampton and South-West Hampshire Health Authority.

It is made up of one small town and 24 parishes with a total population of approximately 40,000. There is a small community hospital in the town. The GPs serving the population are all part of a total purchasing project. It was chosen as an intervention area for the following reasons:

- single person pensioner households have increased by 41 per cent between 1981–91
- pensioner-only households are forming just over a fifth of all households, which from 1981–91 brought an increase of 180 per cent
- the greatest proportional increase in population is in older people aged over 75, amounting to just under 46 per cent of the local population.

To ensure commitment to the proposed work by local agencies it was necessary to get the local Health For All Group known as the Healthy Romsey Group to prioritise accident prevention in their 1997 action plans.

Objectives

- To raise awareness of the local population to the risks in their home which could contribute to an accident.
- To train both carers and health professionals in accident prevention.

Planning and programme design

The following work was agreed by the Healthy Romsey Group:

- development of a home-check leaflet
- involvement of local pharmacists and opticians in distributing the home check leaflet
- distribution of leaflets through venues older people were known to use
- training of carers in awareness of the causes of accidents
- developing oportunities to talk to older people in social settings.

Description of work

The home check leaflet – *Is your home safe enough?*

The leaflet was written by a multi-disciplinary group including a district nurse, health visitor, health promotion specialist, an older resident of Romsey and a nurse from A & E. The draft leaflet was circulated to a wider group of professionals and older people for comments and identified amendments made.

The local pharmacy representative from Southampton and South-West Hampshire Health Authority agreed that the leaflet could be available through all pharmacies, opticians and dentists. So, in November 1997, all pharmacies and opticians were visited by a project worker and given leaflets for distribution to *all* adult customers. Pharmacists in particular were asked to attach a leaflet to every prescription dispensed to an adult during November 1997.

All adults were targeted because it was felt that the leaflet was appropriate for all ages and would raise the awareness of younger people to the risks in the homes of friends and relations. At the same time, information was given both verbally and in written form to pharmacy staff to stress the importance of patients not mixing medicines and alcohol.

During November 1997, 4500 leaflets were distributed to a pre-arranged list of outlets including the local hardware store, Women's Institute Market, luncheon clubs and the local GPs and hospital.

Interestingly there were only four opticians and only one was on the ground floor, consequently, they see most of the elderly population.

All four pharmacies were very keen to be involved in the initiative and it was usually the assistant who took on the role of the distribution of leaflets.

Partnership support

The initiative is supported by a local off-shoot of the main Healthy Romsey Group with representation from:

- Age Concern
- The Sitting Service
- The Council of Community Service
- District nursing
- Health promotion services

Population/age/gender

The people primarily targeted are those aged 60 and above, but the leaflet is suitable for all adults.

Training

Little local training in accident prevention had taken place prior to 1997. It was decided to develop two levels of training to meet local needs. Health promotion specialists started by training a group made up of social workers, district nurses, health visitors and volunteers in accident prevention. The training took place over one day and was advertised in the annual training calendar.

Professional worker sessions

The aims of the day were:

- to assist the participants to have a greater understanding of the emotional, psychological and social impact of accidents on older people
- to learn about effective interventions to reduce the risk of accidents in older people
- to identify ways in which knowledge can be put into practice.

The day was designed to be participative, and enjoyable but with a good grounding in research and effective interventions.

The content of the day included:

- accident statistics – national and local
- emotional impact of accidents
- presentations on two research papers
- the *Home safety* video (as before)
- effective interventions
- exercise and older people
- alcohol and older people
- two further research papers.

Carers sessions

Age Concern approached health promotion services with a request for a session for their workers who act as carers, cleaners and sitters for the elderly in Romsey.

The style of the session was to be informal and had to be delivered to fit in with participants' commitments such as collecting children from school. Information about the session was to be distributed by local organisers and participants were to attend in their own time.

In order to encourage attendance, attractive flyers were developed together with certificates for attendance.

The session content was designed to be participative and unthreatening, and to run from 1.00 p.m. to 3.30 p.m.

The aim was to raise awareness about the main causes of falling and how carers can work with older people to make changes both in their behaviour and environment.

The content of the session was as follows:

- introductions
- a round of risks I have taken this week
- discussion in pairs using scenario cards about everyday situations, for example:
  'Imagine yourself as a 70–75-year-old, someone you know of or one of your clients. How would you feel about asking your neighbour to change a light bulb? Discuss what the consequences of not doing it will be.'
- information on why people fall – using research findings
- a fit-break and discussion on the role of exercise in preventing falls
- information on how we can prevent falls
- video *Home safety* – Southampton City Council
- discussion on how I may change my practice.

Two sessions have been run for seven and eight participants.

As Age Concern have approximately 60 workers, training sessions will need to be run regularly, however, it would be preferable if the participants were paid to attend the sessions to ensure attendance.

Evaluation

The leaflet

The evaluation of the leaflet was qualitative and carried out by a telephone survey to pharmacists asking for feedback received from their customers given the leaflet. The majority of respondents had received positive comments.

District nurses evaluated the leaflet using a simple questionnaire in patients' homes,

The results were very positive and a few of the comments were as follows:

- 'Reminded me of things I had not thought of.'
- 'I felt the leaflet wasn't just useful for older people but also for young families.'
- 'It reassured me that my safety measures in the home were adequate.'
- 'My son made some changes for me after reading the leaflet.'

Ninety-eight per cent of respondents found the leaflet useful and 60 per cent had made some changes to their homes.

The leaflet is now being used across the whole of the Southampton district.

Professional worker sessions

The evaluation was by questionnaire on the day and the results showed the course was a success. However, feedback from the group was that they want less research and more on exercise.

Health promotion services are fortunate to have as a trainer on the benefits of physical activity, Dr Derek Browne, and have since received several requests for talks from him.

Carers' sessions

These were evaluated by the participants in a closing round at the training. All participants felt it had been useful and requested training in other topic areas.

Since running the training, health promotion specialists have also attended two community lunches as guest speakers in accident prevention.

Each person attending the lunch was given a short quiz which asked five questions on home safety, there were multiple choice answers. After lunch, the quiz papers were collected and marked while a health promotion specialist gave a short talk on accident prevention in the home.

A prize of an *Active for Life* umbrella was given to the first correct answer out of a hat.

Invitations to attend several similar events have been a result of the success of the first community lunch.

All forms of training have been well evaluated and requests for places on the next course for professionals have exceeded our proposed maximum.

Funding

All the work was carried out as part of existing workload and the only cost incurred was in printing the home check leaflet. This was provided by health promotion services, as was the co-ordinating role that was the responsibility of a senior health promotion specialist and a project worker. The cost of producing the leaflet was £410.00.

Outcomes/recommendations/future plans

The initiative in Romsey is at a very early stage and has just started to raise awareness of the needs to help prevent accidents. The plans for the future include:

- undertaking a local needs assessment to inform and influence future work
- introducing a local home check scheme to be funded by the local authority
- to develop jointly between Romsey and the New Forest an investigation on the effects of isolation on the health of older people and share information on effective interventions
- to identify some joint local working between the local hospital and the health promotion service on the issue of falls.

An outcome from the training has been the increasing interest in developing physical activity initiatives for older people by leisure providers. This will be a priority for local action shared by the local Age Concern Branch during 1998.

The leaflet has since gone on the essential leaflet list for pharmacies in 1998 and is now being used across Southampton's pharmacies and opticians. It is intended to evaluate the views of these two professions.

Contact

Christine Stiling
Manager
Health Promotion Services
Oatlands House
Winchester Road
Southampton, Hants SO1 5NB

Tel: 01703 784278
Fax: 01703 701489

Making medicine-taking safer: an Avon area conference exploring approaches to improve the safety of older people

Categories: Service Provision, Research and audit, Education

Executive summary

Medication is known to be a strong predictive risk factor in the incidence of falls among older people. The 'Avonsafe–Action for Safety Alliance' organised a multi-disciplinary conference to encourage discussion on the management of medication for older people. The conference evaluation demonstrated that there is much to be done in this area and provided a 'springboard' for future action.

Background

The Avonsafe–Action for Safety Alliance for Older People identified the need for a study day based on the theme of medication and accidents, and set up a multi-agency sub-group to address the issues of concern. Generally it was accepted that whilst there are some examples of good local practice it was 'patchy' with regard to:

- hospital discharge and medication needs and the provision of information to patients
- community systems related to prescribing by the GP and dispensing by the pharmacist – this would include the use of dossette boxes, blister packs etc.
- written instruction regarding medication – explanation and understanding of medication by the patient
- responsibilities concerning the above, that is, whose role?
- storing and taking several different types of medication – safety and side-effects.

The link between medication and the incidence of falls in people over the age of 65 years is well documented. Tinetti *et al.* (1994) in a randomised controlled study of a prospective falls reduction programme for high-risk patients, discovered that patients who took four or more medications were more likely to fall than people taking less. A new syncope service in Bristol sees almost 30 per cent of patients with recurrent unexplained falls who have been taking medications which can cause abnormal cardiovascular responses resulting in 'drop attacks'. Many patients respond to cessation of these 'culprit medications' and some may not have ever needed them. Medical review of patients and especially those who have fallen would seem to have potential for improved patient care. A fall may signal a need to review clinical state, both physical and psychological and would include medication (Dow *et al.* 1997).

The Avonsafe group planned a study day as a starting point to raise awareness of the issues locally.

The aim of the day was:

> to improve the safety of older people by providing a forum for sharing information and good practice relating to medication and accident prevention, and to make recommendations for future action.

The target audience was healthcare professionals and others involved in medicines and care management of older people e.g. GPs, nurses, pharmacists, social services, voluntary agencies and carers. As general practice sees three times more falls-related accidents than hospital services (Graham, H. J. *et al.*, 1992) it was considered important to invite GPs and the conference was PGEA approved.

The planning group was primarily multi-professional (although the main Avonsafe Alliance is multi-agency). The group consisted of a core membership of pharmacists, clinical care co-ordinators, health visitors for the elderly, secretary of the local pharmaceutical committee, community liaison OT, a health promotion specialist, a counsellor from the alcohol advisory service, a representation from the health authority and the community health council.

The programme:

09.00 – 10.00	Registration, coffee and poster session
10.00 – 10.15	Welcome and introductions David Johnstone Acting Chair, Avon Health Authority
10.15 - 10.50	Medication management Dr Michael J. Rowe MD FRCP FRCPE Medical Director, Bath and West Community NHS Trust
10.50 – 11.00	Questions
11.00 – 11.45	Falls, syncope and culprit medications Dr Margaret MacMahon MD Consultant Physician in Medicine, Bristol Royal Infirmary
11.45 – 12.15	Questions to the panel
12.15 – 12.30	Closing remarks and workshop preparation
12.30 – 1.30	Lunch and poster session
1.30 – 2.45	Workshops
Workshop 1	Polypharmacy and prescription review Trevor Beswick, Regional Pharmaceutical Adviser NHSE South and West

Workshop 2	Managing primary/secondary care interface Jenny Treadwell, Community Care Facilitator UBHT
Workshop 3	Rights responsibilities and information for patients and carers Tony Jones, The Local Voices Project, managed by the community health council
Workshop 4	Primary healthcare team management of medication Pat Turton – Primary Care Lecturer, University of Bristol
2.45 – 3.00	Tea and poster session
3.00 – 3.50	Workshop feedback
3.50 – 4.00	Closing remarks Chair

Evaluation

The conference was evaluated by inviting delegates to fill in self-completion question-naires, which were collated for the consideration of the planning group. Eighty people attended the conference and 54 evaluation forms were returned.

The workshop proceedings and a summary of the evaluations were sent to all the dele-gates. The evaluations on the whole were extremely positive and whilst not providing solu-tions many recommendations were made for future action. Some lessons were learned, for example having older people present at the conference would have added an essential con-sumer perspective. Some press coverage was achieved. (Copies of the conference pack are available on request from the contact person listed).

Funding

The initiative was funded by delegates paying a fee of £10 to attend. The conference was also sponsored by four different drug companies, and subsidised by the local pharmaceuti-cal committee.

Outcomes/recommendations/future plans

Medicine Safety and Older People is an agreed priority in the Avonsafe–Action for Safety Strategy 1997–2000. The work will be sustained and the conference provided a 'spring-board for action'. There were many important recommendations from the conference which can be summarised into three key areas for future consideration. These are:

• work in this area should be multi-disciplinary – the conference highlighted the need for improved practice across all disciplines and recommended that joint training should be developed;

- communication is the key – sharing of information between professionals is vital;
- the need for pharmacists to take on a much wider community role – and the importance of recognition/interaction between GP/pharmacist on medication and compliance issues.

References

Tinetti, M., Baker, D. J., McAvay, G., Claus, E. B., Garrat, P., Gottschalk, M., Koch, M. L., Trainer Horwitz, T. I. (1994) A multi-factorial intervention to reduce the risk of falling among elderly people living in the community. *The New England Journal of Medicine* **331** (13): 821–7.

Dow, L., Harker, P. and Wright, P., (1997) *Primary care to reduce falls in older people – Briefing review number 6.* Health Promotion Research Programme, Department of Social Medicine: University of Bristol.

Graham, H. J. and Firth, J. (1992) Home accidents in older people role of primary health care team. *British Medical Journal* **305**: 30–2.

Avonsafe Alliance–Avonsafe Accident Prevention Alliance Strategy 1997–2000 (1997) (unpublished).

Contact

Maggie Sims
Senior Health Promotion Specialist – Accident Prevention
Health Promotion Service Avon
Henshaw House
Cossham Hospital
Lodge Road
Kingswood
Bristol BS15 1LF

Tel: 0117 975 8031
Fax: 0117 975 8011
e-mail: hpsa@netcomuk.co.uk

Free smoke alarms for older people: an initiative in the Avon Fire Brigade area

Categories: Service Provision, Education and Training

Start date: 17 April 1997
Completion date: April 2002

Executive summary

Older people are most at risk from death and injury due to fire in their own homes. The Avon Fire Brigade, working in partnership with other agencies and organisations will, over a five-year period, provide and fit, free of charge, at least one smoke alarm at each level of every home (in the brigade area) where the occupier is aged 65 years or over and who currently does not have one.

Description of the work

It is a fact that older people are most at risk from death and injury as a result of fire in their own homes. There are a number of reasons for this: in particular their having less tolerance of the effects of burns and smoke than young people; they are more likely to have fires; their mobility and associated reaction; and the fact that they are less able to tackle an incipient fire or make their escape from fire should the need arise.

- In the UK in 1994, 48.4 per cent of those who died from fire in the home were aged 60 years or over.
- In the UK in 1994, 242 people aged 60 years or over died in fires and around 3110 were injured by fire in their own homes.
- In Avon in 1994, three people (50 per cent) aged 60 years or over died in fires in their own home out of a total of six.

Aims and objectives

During 1996, a survey was carried out by brigade fire safety officers, talking to groups of older people at day centres etc. to gather information as to their perceptions of the role of fire and what they would do should a fire break out within their own home. Emphasis was also placed on how they would obtain advice regarding home fire safety.

It was soon recognised that the perception of fire by older people was clearly underestimated and the brigade, therefore, decided that this researched information, supported by the known statistics, demanded that positive action be taken to address the issue of fire safety awareness for older people.

Planning

The brigade understood that the scale of the project was so immense that it could not manage and operate it alone. It needed the support and co-operation of both the public and private sector. The brigade does not have a community fire safety budget on which to draw to fund such initiatives. Although it was recognised that the project would require around £100,000 to succeed, this was not seen as a problem which could not be overcome, or dampen the enthusiasm of the brigade community team. The fact that the project was planned to run for five years would allow for a certain 'flexibility' in fundraising each year.

The project would have to be carried out by volunteers; there was not sufficient time available within the work routine of the brigade to enable support from brigade personnel to be given.

The project was promoted and advertised by using local radio, television and newspaper. To avoid excessive telephone calls the newspaper articles included a self-completion return slip.

Partnership support

A request was made throughout the brigade seeking volunteer support, which resulted in 14 active serving members, and seven retired members. Agencies, organisations and community groups both in the public and private sector were contacted and the following groups are actively working in support of the project:

- Avonsafe Action for Safety Older People Group
- Bristol Age Concern
- Bristol Care and Repair
- Bristol City Council contractors, Bristol Contract Services with whom the brigade joined in partnership to support their 'Safe and Warm' initiative
- The Church of Jesus Christ of Latter Day Saints
- The Duke of Edinburgh Award Scheme
- The Princes Trust
- Rotary clubs
- Rotract clubs.

The project was, therefore, very definitely multi-agency and multi-professional, supporting key objectives identified in the brigade's *Strategy and Operational Plan 1998–2003*, the Avonsafe Accident Prevention Alliance Strategy 1997–2000 as well as national health strategies.

The project was launched on 17 April 1997 supporting the launch of the Avonsafe Accident Prevention Alliance Strategy where an invited audience of health professionals, local authority personnel, members from those organisations listed above, the emergency services and other statutory and voluntary groups committed to the project attended. The launch attracted good coverage from the local media.

Population/age/gender

There were to be no criteria for exemption from the project. This was considered to be the fairest and least intrusive way of gaining the confidence and trust of older people, whilst understanding that all are potentially at risk from fire.

The target was to provide and fit free of charge at least one smoke alarm at each level of every home (in the brigade area) where the occupier is aged 65 years or over (male or female) and who currently does not have one. It was estimated that this would target around 20,000 homes fitting around 30,000 alarms.

Funding

Projected costings required to be raised within the time frame of the project determined the sum around £200,000. The brigade approached organisations seeking financial support. This was successful from:

• The Dolphin Society	£10,000	Recurring
• Health Promotion Service Avon	£1000	Non recurring
• GWR Radio	£1000	Non recurring
• Great Mills	Equipment	Recurring
• Black and Decker	Equipment	Recurring

The support from the Dolphin Society was greatly appreciated, this now meant that the project could realistically 'take off'. What also became apparent was the kind generosity of the older people themselves. Although fully aware that the project was provided absolutely free of charge, many insisted on making small financial contributions, which were invested back into the project.

The brigade would fund the issue of ID cards to all volunteers together with the specific working overalls and associated advertising and publicity of the project. Dedicated officer time, some resources, the management, administration and training of volunteers, all supported by the brigade. The local media also offered free publicity.

Smoke alarms were purchased from First Alert at highly competitive rates who also provided, free of charge, individual sticky labels for each householder to have printed the month for alarm battery replacement.

A specific type of smoke alarm was purchased i.e. a torch test type, which meant that for testing purposes, older people could test their alarm from ground level, with a torch, and not have to balance on an unsafe chair or stool in order to press the test button.

Evaluation

It was agreed by all parties that the question of evaluation should be addressed early into the project to determine its success or otherwise. It was established that a true evaluation should be both quantitative and qualitative. The following were identified as a means of researching and collecting accurate information for evaluation:

- collate a register of all applicants
- record how each applicant knew about the project
- record how many homes have been fitted with an alarm/s
- record how many alarms have been fitted
- seek from management information services (fire safety headquarters) details of every domestic fire involving an occupier 65 years of age or over
- seek to establish whether the home had a smoke alarm/s fitted
- was it/they fitted through the project
- seek to find out whether they were in working order
- seek to find out whether they activated due to the fire
- seek to find out whether they ensured the safety of the occupier in warning of the fire and promoting their escape
- did it/they save a life?

A follow-up evaluation will need to be carried out in selected areas to determine whether battery testing/maintenance is being carried out regularly as well as battery replacement.

Training

The success of the project would depend upon appropriate training being provided to all volunteer groups and individuals. This initiated a training programme by brigade community officers visiting all volunteers and volunteer groups to explain the project procedures. The use of ID cards, the wearing of the specific working overalls, the fitting of the alarms, the fire safety advice to be given to the occupier which includes the alarm testing and battery replacement principle. Brigade community officers were to accompany all volunteers and volunteer groups on their initial visit to fit smoke alarms to provide support, comfort and advice.

Outcomes/recommendations/future plans

Since the launch of the project 3000 alarms have been purchased (17 April 1997–31 March 1998) together with 20 specialist alarm sets for the hard of hearing. And 2600 alarms have been fitted in 1450 homes. Certainly lessons have been learnt during the operation of the project:

- the recruitment of volunteers in sufficient numbers to carry out the fitting programme took longer than was first anticipated by the brigade itself, although there was no lack of volunteer support from voluntary organisations;

- for successful management and control of such a large project it is important that accurate and constantly updated records are kept. Applications occasionally arrived in their hundreds, which required patient and systematic recording at that time;

- the project should be publicised in phases so that the early responding applicants do not have to wait an excessively long time for their alarm/s to be fitted. It is very easy to be drawn into 'queue jumping'.

The planned intention at the end of the five-year project is to continue the initiative but aim the project to target the 60-65 year age group. This again would mean seeking further volunteer support and sponsorship, however, hopefully the enthusiasm, commitment, and proven success of the existing project would enable the 'wheels be kept in motion'.

The scheme has been extended to address the issue of families with children under the age of five living in areas of high health need. Again, ownership of a smoke alarm/s has proven not to be high on their list of priorities and so, working in partnership with Avonsafe Action for Safety and Health Centres in the Avon area the brigade is supporting 'Low Cost Safety Equipment Schemes'. This project enables parents to save £1 a week at their Health Centre and after four weeks purchase a smoke alarm which brigade personnel will fit free of charge.

Contact

John Sleight
Assistant Divisional Officer
Senior Community Fire Safety Officer
Fire Safety Headquarters
Lansdown Road
Lansdown
Bath
BA1 9DA

Tel: 0117 9262061
Fax: 01225 460025

Empowerment of older people in Bristol and Calne through the arts (pilot study)

Category: Needs assessment

Start date: September 1996 and ongoing

Executive summary

Empowerment of Older People through the Arts (EOPTA) was developed with the aim of using the arts to enable the active group participation of isolated older people, empowering them to articulate their health needs in relation to housing. Whilst being creative, learning new skills and having fun, participants gained self-confidence and self-esteem through group membership and began to address issues relating to housing, safety and independence through their work. The photography group used cameras to record potential hazards in their homes and adaptations which were made to increase their independence, whilst members of the quilting group joined the management committee of Care and Repair and other local fora in order to voice their opinions about the housing and safety needs of older people.

Description of work

Two projects were developed, a quilting project based in Care and Repair, Bristol and a photography project based in Calne, Wiltshire. Management of the project was carried out by a steering group who employed an independent arts consultant to evaluate the work.

The quilting project was set up as a support group for users of Bristol Care and Repair, with the main aim of empowering participants to become more involved in the development and management of the service. An associated aim was to relieve the isolation that many owners occupiers experience when they are dependent on a low income, with limited access to information, transport, leisure facilities and social contact.

The photography project was the work of an alliance between Age Concern, the local authority, Anchor Staying Put, Council for Voluntary Service and health promotion. The aim was to give isolated older people the opportunity to use photography and image making to explore ideas about housing issues, particularly focusing on their experiences of living in rural villages in Wiltshire.

Population

Initially there were 24 project participants aged from their 60s to their 90s and over 85 per cent were women. They came from a variety of ethnic backgrounds and had a range of physical and mental health problems. Most lived alone and all were socially isolated.

Funding

The quilting project was funded primarily through a grant from Comic Relief of £5000.

The photography project received funding from a variety of organisations including Help the Aged, Housing 21, Southern Arts, North Wiltshire District Council, YAPP Charitable Trusts, HACT and the Averil Osborne Fund.

The project cost approximately £9000.

Evaluation

The project was fully evaluated by an independent arts consultant using a variety of methods including interviews with participants, steering group members and artists, diaries and questionnaires. A full evaluation report is available on request.

Outcomes

- Participants from the quilting group have joined Bristol Care and Repairs' Management Committee.
- Participants have become active members of Bristol Older People's Forum and spoken at a number of conferences on housing issues for older people.
- Bristol Care and Repair are now setting up more arts-based user groups around the city.
- The photography project is now being developed to include video and archive work, involving younger people from local schools and youth clubs.
- The work of the group has been exhibited in a variety of local venues including the housing association, the tourist information centre and a local arts centre.
- An umbrella project is now being planned to co-ordinate arts health work for older people across Wiltshire, working with a variety of agencies including Age Concern and local authorities.

The positive outcomes of these projects have added to the increasing body of work showing that the active involvement of older people in arts activities has a profound effect on individuals. There is certainly a need for more long-term and strategic work to be done in the field of older people, empowerment and the arts.

By disseminating information about this project it is hoped to inspire others to adopt a positive and creative approach to work with older people.

Main contacts

Photography

Cathy Lees
Wiltshire Health Promotion Service
Oak House
Greenways Centre
Malmesbury Road
Chippenham
Wiltshire
SN15 5LN

Tel: 01249 454270
Fax: 01249 454271
e-mail oak@chipoff.wilthp.btinternet.com

Quilting

Maggie Sims
Health Promotion Service Avon
Henshaw House
Cossham Hospital
Lodge Road
Kingswood Bristol
BS15 1LF

Tel: 0117 975 8031
Fax: 0117 975 8011